—GUID

C A L I F O R N I A ' S
MARINE LIFE
MANAGEMENT ACT

SECOND EDITION

MICHAEL L. WEBER
Program Officer, Resources Legacy Fund

BURR HENEMAN

HUFF McGONIGAL
Principal, Fathom Consulting

2018
CALIFORNIA WILDLIFE FOUNDATION
OAKLAND, CALIFORNIA

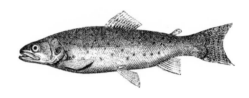

ISBN: 978-0-9996769-0-5 (paperback)
978-0-9996769-1-2 (PDF)

Weber, Michael L., Heneman, Burr, and McGonigal, Huff. 2017.
Guide to California's Marine Life Management Act: Second Edition.

Published by
California Wildlife Foundation
428 13th Street, Suite 10A
Oakland, CA 94612
www.californiawildlifefoundation.org

Book design:
Eric Larson, Studio E Books
Santa Barbara, California

Cover illustration:
Brown rockfish, *Sebastes auriculatus*
Black rockfish, *Sebastes melanops*
Fish print by Christopher M. Dewees

Interior fish and shellfish © Paul B. Johnson
California Department of Fish and Game

CONTENTS

APPENDICES

The passage of the Marine Life Management Act in 1998 marked an important turning point for California's ocean fisheries. The Act, which drew upon successes and failures in fisheries management in previous decades, created the basis for an advanced, progressive system for managing the state's ocean fisheries. Through the hard work of the Department of Fish and Wildlife, the Fish and Game Commission, fishermen, scientists, conservationists, and other stakeholders, California has moved firmly in the direction of management informed by the best science and by the knowledge and interests of stakeholders. Californians enjoy some of the most protectively managed fisheries in the world.

Now, Californians face two major challenges to their efforts to maintain fisheries that are ecologically sustainable and that continue to provide diverse benefits to Californians, particularly our coastal communities.

First, the last several years have made plain that California's ocean ecosystems are already experiencing unprecedented shocks as the Earth's changing climate and acidification of ocean waters take hold. Two years ago, a massive algal bloom released domoic acid that contaminated Dungeness crabs and rock crabs, leading to an historic, months-long closure of those fisheries resulting in a federal fisheries disaster declaration. The economic and social impacts of those closures continue to reverberate. Soon after, changes in ocean temperature and chemistry and a wasting disease among sea stars contributed to the destruction of kelp beds and the collapse of the red sea urchin fishery north of San Francisco. We can also expect other, subtler changes as species contend with changing conditions by moving north or into deeper water. In some recent years, market squid, which have long been resident in southern and central California waters, have been found as far north as Oregon.

While the Marine Life Management Act provides the kind of policy tools we will need to confront these challenges and to protect California's fisheries, ecosystems, and fishing communities, we face a second challenge. Put quite simply: The Act's policy tools will remain locked up in the toolbox unless we secure sufficient funding for monitoring, for good science, for enforcement, and for collaboration. Meeting this challenge is the responsibility not simply of fishermen, but of all Californians who benefit from a supply of healthy seafood and from a myriad of benefits healthy marine ecosystems provide.

I'm confident that the second edition of the *Guide to California's Marine Life Management Act* will prove to be a valuable source of information in meeting these challenges.

Warmest Regards,

MIKE McGUIRE
Senator
Chairman Joint Committee on Fisheries and Aquaculture

FOREWORD

WHEN THE MARINE Life Management Act (MLMA) was enacted in 1998, it was an innovative and progressive law that placed new emphasis on ecosystem-based management, sustainability, and stakeholder engagement. The law also expanded the authority of the California Department of Fish and Wildlife and the Fish and Game Commission to make management more comprehensive and strategic.

In the intervening 17 years, both the Department and the Commission have made significant progress towards implementing the MLMA, working to generate new fishery management plans, better integrate science into management, and engage stakeholders in a wide range of management settings. Throughout that time, the first edition of the *Guide to California's Marine Life Management Act* has been a valuable resource for both managers and stakeholders, providing an accessible overview of the act, its goals and strategies.

This second edition is timely in that it coincides with our first amendment to the MLMA Master Plan, the act's implementation roadmap. The revised master plan will build upon the foundation developed over the past 17 years to incorporate new tools and approaches that have been developed since the enactment of the MLMA. The new edition of the guide still provides an excellent overview of the law, but also now includes a review of its implementation to date, as well as lays groundwork for the new path we have just initiated in updating the master plan.

The natural variability of the ocean environment constantly poses a challenge to fishery managers. Climate change is already increasing that challenge and that is likely to increase in the years to come making the adaptive and collaborative vision laid out in the MLMA more important than ever. California is graced with a marine ecosystem as rich as anywhere on earth and has a rich fishing culture that is woven into the history of the state. Stakeholders, managers, and lawmakers need to work closely together to ensure that both are safeguarded for current and future generations. Effective implementation of the MLMA will help inform how the Marine Life Protection Act can inform fisheries management.

As the first edition of the *Guide to California's Marine Life Management Act* has been an essential reference, so too will be the second edition. We highly recommend both a thorough reading of the guide as well as keeping it close at hand for future reference. We are certain you will find the guide extremely useful, just as we have.

Chuck Bonham
DIRECTOR
CALIFORNIA DEPARTMENT OF FISH AND WILDLIFE

Eric Sklar
PRESIDENT
CALIFORNIA FISH AND GAME COMMISSION

PREFACE

IN 2000, BURR Heneman and Mike Weber drafted the first edition of this guide, believing that the success of the Marine Life Management Act and the health of the state's fisheries and its fishing communities would benefit from an active understanding of the law among policy makers and stakeholders. The guide seems to have been embraced in that spirit; it has also been long out of print. Considering the challenges and opportunities California's fisheries now face, and the effort recently launched by the Commission and Department to revise the Master Plan for Fisheries, Huff McGonigal and Mike decided it was time to revise the guide.

The last several years have introduced a new era in California's ocean fisheries, an era in which the unexpected regularly happens and challenges the way in which we manage our use of ocean ecosystems. Whether it's pervasive contamination of Dungeness crab with domoic acid caused by harmful algal blooms, or it's an unprecedented "warm blob" of ocean water that devastates north coast kelp beds and sea urchin fisheries, or it's depressed levels of phytoplankton—food for fish, crabs, birds, dolphins, and whales—the state's ocean ecosystems are undergoing changes that can be forecast only very generally. The days when fishermen and fisheries managers could count on relatively steady environmental conditions seem to be gone. Population models, for example, that might have been informative in the 1980s or 1990s may be unsuited to today's complex and dynamic conditions.

In these circumstances, it may be that the challenge for fisheries managers is not simply securing maximum benefits, but also insulating fisheries from the risks associated with a changing ocean. Rather than accepting that what we have done in the past is a script for the future, perhaps we should consider different scenarios and the risks associated with different management approaches. And we must certainly pay closer attention to what the performance of the state's fisheries and other indicators are saying about trends that will affect fisheries, fishing communities, and the ecosystems they depend upon.

In revising the guide, we have both added to and removed material from the first edition. The second edition includes a more extensive description of the management setting, including international, federal, and state management, tribal management and engagement as well as a description of different sources of funding for fisheries management. The second edition also includes a description of a range of initiatives and tools that might inform how California meets current and future challenges to the sustainability of its fisheries. We have also included several appendices, which present statistical profiles of commercial fisheries, display information about management jurisdictions for different fisheries and restricted access programs, summaries of relevant state and federal fishery management plans, and other topics.

For the immediate future, the three of us hope that this guide helps readers understand the MLMA so that they can more effectively participate in the revision of the master plan that the Commission and Department are undertaking. But we also hope that the guide fosters successful use of the MLMA in advancing the ecological, social, and economic sustainability of the state's ocean fisheries in future years as well.

We are grateful to the reviewers of a draft version of this guide: Tom Barnes, Chris Dewees, Ken Franke, Kaitilin Gaffney, Greg Helms, Joe Milton, Hawk Rosales, Craig Shuman, Bruce Steele, and Nathan Voegeli. Our reviewers' expertise and diversity of perspectives enriched the text immeasurably. We, the authors, are responsible for any remaining errors of fact or interpretation.

Other people provided indispensable assistance. We thank Chuck Bonham, Alexa-Fredston-Hermann, Jordan Maeding, Eric Sklar, Rick Starr, Sarah Valencia, and Tom Weseloh.

This guide is a product of Resources Legacy Fund's California Fisheries Improvement Strategy. We are deeply grateful to the David and Lucile Packard Foundation for its support and for its steadfast commitment to the health of the oceans.

—— GUIDE TO ——

CALIFORNIA'S

MARINE LIFE

MANAGEMENT ACT

— CHAPTER 1 —
CALIFORNIA'S
OCEAN FISHERIES

THE SETTING

FOR 1,100 MILES, the spectacular mass of California's land meets the Pacific Ocean. In many areas of the state, mountains plunge into the ocean. On the coast, ancient shorelines stand as terraces above the surf. Elsewhere, streams and rivers break through the coastal mountains and flow into bays and lagoons rimmed with wetlands. Offshore, islands and rocks break the surface.

This is what we can easily see. But beneath the surface of the 5,767 square statute miles of ocean and bay waters, California's dramatic geological formations continue. Unlike the Atlantic or Gulf coasts, California's shallow continental shelf is quite narrow, generally no wider than five miles. At its broadest point off San Francisco, the shelf extends 30 miles offshore before plunging from 600 feet to the abyssal region at 6,000 feet. Here and there, peaks called seamounts rise from the depths to the photic zone where sunlight spurs plant growth and attracts life.

Whether near or far from shore, the ocean bottom may be rocky, sandy, or silty. It may be flat or formed of rocky reefs. In many areas along the coast, great canyons cut into the continental shelf, some quite close to shore. For example, the Monterey Submarine Canyon, which is larger than the Grand Canyon of the Colorado, begins within miles of the shoreline. There, as at other submarine canyons, marine life normally found far offshore is drawn close to land by the deep waters. Off southern California, the ocean bottom consists of basins, troughs, canyons, peaks, and cliffs alternating in a checkerboard pattern.

Ocean currents introduce other dimensions to California's coastal waters. For much of the year, the California Current brings cool northern waters southward along the shore as far as southern California. There,

3

where the coastline juts eastward, the California Current moves offshore. In the gap between the California Current and the mainland, the Southern California Countercurrent flows into the Santa Barbara Channel. Around Point Conception, these two currents meet, creating a rich transition zone. Closer to shore and deeper, the California Undercurrent also carries warmer water northward.

Seasonal changes in wind direction commonly create seasonal patterns for these currents. In March, for instance, northwesterly winds usually begin and combine with the rotation of the Earth to drive surface waters offshore, triggering the upwelling of cold, nutrient-rich water from the depths. Fueled by sunlight and the nutrients, single-celled algae bloom and create a rich soup that fuels a blossoming of marine life, attracting larger animals from seabirds and swordfish to humpback and blue whales.

By September, as the northwesterly winds die down, the cold water sinks again and warmer waters return to the coast. This oceanic period typically lasts into October, when the winds move to the southwesterly direction. These winds drive a surface current, called the Davidson Current, which flows north of Point Conception and inside the California Current, generally lasting through February.

Laid over this general pattern are both short-term and long-term shifts. Local winds, topography, tidal motions, and discharge from rivers create their own currents in nearshore waters. Less frequently, a massive change in atmospheric pressure off Australia floods the eastern Pacific with warm water, which suppresses the normal pattern of upwelling. These short-term climatic changes, called El Niño, reduce the productivity of coastal waters, causing some fisheries and seabirds and marine mammal populations to decline. El Niños can also increase the abundance of other species. For instance, warm waters that flow north in an El Niño carry the larva of sheephead and lobster from the heart of their geographical range in Mexico into the waters off California.

Other oceanographic changes last for a decade or more. In these regime shifts, water temperatures rise or fall significantly, causing dramatic changes in the distribution and abundance of marine life. The collapse of the California sardine fishery occurred when heavy fishing continued on sardine populations that were greatly reduced by a cooling of offshore waters in the late 1940s and early 1950s. In response to the decline in sardines, California law severely curtailed the catch. In 1977, waters off California began warming and remained relatively warm. The warmer water temperatures were favorable for sardines, whose abundance greatly increased. But the warmer waters also reduced the productivity of other fish, including many rockfish, lingcod, sablefish, and most flatfish, which favor cold water for successful reproduction.

Since the MLMA was passed, the impacts of climate change, and more recently of ocean acidification, have made themselves felt ever more dramatically. In 2016, the West Coast Ocean Acidification and Hypoxia Panel, convened by the California Ocean Science Trust (OST) at the request of the Ocean Protection Council (OPC), released its report outlining likely impacts of ocean acidification on west coast ocean ecosystems. Among other things, the panel found that increasing acidification will jeopardize shell-forming species, ranging from oysters to plankton upon which ocean food webs are based.

In 2014–2016, an unprecedented "blob" of warm water expanded and persisted along the west coast of North America, disrupting coastal ecosystems. The Dungeness crab fishery, one of California's most valuable, was closed for much of the 2015–2016 season due to an unprecedented harmful algal bloom. Populations of market squid, which previously were rarely found north of San Francisco, shifted as far north as Oregon and beyond. Along the coast north of San Francisco, kelp beds vanished in the warm water, leaving abalone and urchins without forage and important finfish species without shelter.

Concerns about the economic dislocation caused by these events and about possible recurrence in the future spurred engagement by the legislature's Joint Committee on Fisheries and Aquaculture. The OPC responded by requesting that the California OST work with counterparts in Oregon, Washington, and British Columbia to convene a task force on climate change and ocean acidification. The OPC also directed its Science Advisory Team to develop guidance for managing fisheries in the face of climate change and ocean acidification.

MARINE LIFE OF CALIFORNIA

The waters off California are host to 544 species of fish from 144 families. Thousands of species of marine invertebrates inhabit the sea floor from tidepools along the shoreline to muddy plains 8,000 feet deep. Dozens of species of coastal and offshore birds spend some part of the year in

California's waters, as do 35 species of marine mammals, and several species of sea turtles.

This great variety of marine life reflects the different responses of groups of animals and plants to changing environmental conditions over long periods of time. In successfully meeting their needs for growth, survival, and reproduction, individual species have developed a set of characteristics that biologists call life history traits. These traits include age at maturity, maximum age, maximum size, growth rate, natural mortality, and feeding and reproductive strategies.

Differences among species can be dramatic. For instance, California market squid mature within 12 months and die soon after spawning, whereas yelloweye rockfish do not mature until the age of 20 at the earliest and may live as long as 120 years. This has profound consequences for managing fisheries.

Reproductive strategies also vary. Queenfish, for instance, may spawn 24 times in a season, releasing their body weight in eggs into the open water, where most eggs will be eaten whether or not they are fertilized. In contrast, species such as olive rockfish spawn just once a year, releasing larvae, which have been fertilized and developed internally.

Amid the variety, the life histories of fish tend to fall into several larger categories. For instance, fish species that have low rates of mortality as adults, such as many species of sharks, bluefin tuna, billfish, and rockfish, also mature late and reproduce in smaller numbers. Organisms that have high rates of mortality as adults, such as anchovies and squid, grow quickly, mature early, and reproduce in large numbers.

Species differ also in their movements. For instance, during winter Dover sole move into deep water where they reproduce, then move into shallow water in the summer to feed. Pacific whiting migrate from their summer feeding grounds off Oregon and Washington to their winter spawning grounds off southern California and Baja California. By contrast, kelp bass, which can live to 30 years, venture less than a mile from their home range.

Individual plants and animals are part of larger communities that are linked in many ways. One of the clearest is the relationship between who eats whom, also known as the food web. Generally, the eating begins with herbivores, who consume plants that have manufactured food through photosynthesis. These herbivores may be as small as the larva of an anchovy or as large as a basking shark. The smaller herbivores pass along much of the food value of the plants when they are eaten by primary carnivores. In some marine communities, the story may end here. But the eating generally continues several more steps.

These relationships among wildlife populations differ considerably among different habitats and communities. A decrease in the abundance of some species, due to fishing, habitat alteration, or climate changes, for instance, can affect species that feed upon them. Considering these inter-relationships when managing fisheries requires an ecosystem perspective.

Healthy habitat can also play an important role in the abundance of marine wildlife. Some species of fish and shellfish are so dependent upon particular types of habitat, such as kelp forests or coastal wetlands, that the destruction of these habitats can devastate wild populations. The damming of almost every major coastal river in California has driven most runs of Pacific salmon to dangerously low levels. Since the 1850s, 90 percent of the state's coastal wetlands have been destroyed, causing incalculable losses in coastal wildlife. Finally, pollution of coastal waters can expose marine animals to toxic chemicals and can foster changes in plant communities that wildlife depend upon.

A STATISTICAL PROFILE OF CALIFORNIA'S COMMERCIAL FISHERIES

California's commercial fishing history is both long and rich. Fishing has played an important role in shaping communities and culture along the coast, since the earliest human habitation of the state. Commercial fisheries first arose around the time of the Gold Rush in 1850 when thousands of immigrants flooded into California. The ports of San Francisco and Monterey in particular became home to Italian fishermen fishing from small sail boats for herring, salmon, sturgeon, smelts, and other species. In the twentieth century, commercial fisheries grew rapidly as canneries emerged, in the first half of the century for sardine in Monterey and in the second half for tuna in San Pedro and San Diego. For a time, the Pacific sardine fishery was the largest in the world. While fluctuations in fish populations and market forces led to the decline of these industrial-scale fisheries and the canneries they supported, a diversity of smaller-scale fisheries developed in their shadow. Each of California's ports became home to a unique mix of fisheries shaped by local species, markets, and fishermen.

Below is a brief profile of these fisheries and how they've changed over the last ten years. For more port and region-specific information, please see Appendix F.

California's marine fisheries are diverse and can fluctuate dramatically. In 2014, California commercial fishermen reported landing more than 225 species of fish and shellfish. (See Table 1.) Although many species were caught in waters off California, other species, such as skipjack, yellowfin, and albacore tunas, swordfish, and pink shrimp, were caught in waters off other states or off other countries. In terms of weight and the revenues they generate for fishermen, a few species dominated landings in California, according to statistics collected from fish dealers by Department staff and maintained by the Pacific States Marine Fisheries Commission. In 2014, California fishermen landed 358 million pounds of fish and shellfish for which they were paid $235 million; by comparison, fishermen landed more than 553 million pounds in 2000, and were paid $136 million. A number of factors contributed to these trends, such as a dramatic decline in landings of high-value groundfish and salmon, a shift to large volume but low-priced invertebrate fisheries, and increased prices for some species with high market demand abroad, such as spiny lobster. (See Table 2.) In 2014, prices for the top 20 species ranged from seven cents per pound for Pacific mackerel to $19.11 per pound for California spiny lobster. Ranked in order of revenues, as recorded by the California Fishery Information System, the top 20 species in 2014 were as shown in Table 1.

All told, these species accounted for 93 percent of the weight and nearly 95 percent of the revenue from fish and shellfish landed by commercial fishermen in California in 2014. Statistics for the 2000 season, the year after the MLMA went into effect, show similarities but striking differences as well, as shown in Table 2. Although the weight of landings in 2000 was substantially greater than 2014 landings, the revenues were much less in 2000. This is explained partly by dramatic increases in prices for some species. For example, the price per pound for spiny lobster increased from $6.63 in 2000 to $19.11 in 2014, while California halibut increased from $2.88 to $5.50.

For statistical purposes, California's commercial fishing ports are grouped into nine port areas. Table 3 shows the port areas ranked by revenues from commercial landings in 2014.

TABLE 1: TOP 20 COMMERCIAL FISHERIES BY VOLUME AND VALUE IN 2014

SPECIES	POUNDS	VALUE	PRICE/LB
Market squid	227,799,383	$72,382,617	$0.32
Dungeness crab	18,370,199	$66,806,540	$3.64
Spiny lobster	951,393	$18,180,286	$19.11
Red sea urchin	11,842,341	$9,116,581	$0.77
Sablefish	3,611,212	$8,962,574	$2.48
Spot prawn	423,719	$5,355,465	$12.64
Ocean pink shrimp	8,476,677	$4,334,173	$0.51
Longspine thornyhead	829,356	$3,087,784	$3.72
Nearshore finfish*	468,197	$2,570,904	$5.49
Shortspine thornyhead	834,926	$2,216,119	$2.65
California halibut	386,671	$2,126,431	$5.50
Pacific sardine	17,125,439	$2,000,814	$0.12
Dover sole	4,288,818	$1,906,852	$0.44
Red rock crab	1,087,036	$1,658,136	$1.53
Petrale sole	1,348,645	$1,641,940	$1.22
Northern anchovy	23,172,146	$1,619,985	$0.07
Albacore tuna	798,080	$1,604,173	$2.01
Bigeye tuna	406,477	$1,517,130	$3.73
Ridgeback prawn	534,288	$1,502,574	$2.81
Pacific mackerel	11,958,434	$1,227,154	$0.10
Total top 20 species	334,713,437	$209,818,232	
Total all CA species	357,566,848	$235,219,493	

*Nearshore finfish are the 19 species of rockfish and other nearshore species included in the Nearshore Fishery Management Plan.

**TABLE 2: TOP 20 COMMERCIAL FISHERIES
BY VOLUME AND VALUE IN 2000**

SPECIES	POUNDS	VALUE	PRICE/LB
Market squid	261,940,567	$27,105,225	$0.10
Red sea urchin	15,166,155	$14,917,308	$0.98
Dungeness crab	6,492,910	$13,732,227	$2.11
Swordfish	4,048,187	$11,705,551	$2.89
Chinook salmon	5,134,588	$10,274,675	$2.00
Pacific sardine	118,192,953	$5,460,211	$0.05
Sablefish	4,136,065	$5,257,110	$1.27
Spiny lobster	705,704	$4,679,999	$6.63
Albacore tuna	4,150,686	$3,826,186	$0.92
Spot prawn	447,124	$3,814,915	$8.53
Nearshore finfish*	908,535	$3,533,739	$3.89
Pacific mackerel	48,316,798	$2,923,940	$0.06
Dover sole	7,307,213	$2,482,097	$0.34
California halibut	847,521	$2,443,480	$2.88
Pacific herring roe	7,604,982	$2,283,839	$0.30
Longspine thornyhead	1,964,031	$1,943,291	$0.99
Ridgeback prawn	1,565,009	$1,780,712	$1.14
Petrale sole	1,411,037	$1,443,559	$1.02
Rock crab	1,088,160	$1,390,479	$1.28
Northern anchovy	25,911,754	$1,352,218	$0.05
Total top 20 species	517,339,979	$122,350,761	
Total all CA species	553,462,949	$136,320,339	

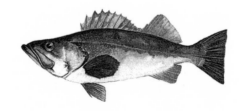

TABLE 3: VOLUME AND VALUE OF COMMERCIAL LANDINGS BY PORT AREA IN 2014

PORT AREA	POUNDS	VALUE
San Francisco	40,760,733	$45,925,122
Santa Barbara	82,197,796	$44,500,906
Monterey	130,747,079	$40,317,638
Eureka	25,301,099	$31,625,251
Los Angeles	55,862,018	$24,312,130
Fort Bragg	8,857,427	$14,356,515
Bodega Bay	4,311,471	$13,416,636
Morro Bay	7,185,470	$10,458,256
San Diego	2,343,754	$10,307,038
Total	357,566,848	$235,219,493

The general ranking of the ports has not changed much since 2000, with the exception of the Los Angeles port area, which led all others in 2000 by a wide margin but now ranks fifth—a shift reflecting a dramatic decline in landings of market squid and Pacific sardine at Los Angeles area ports. The lumping of individual ports into port areas obscures significant differences in scale. For example, in the Eureka port area, commercial landings in Eureka generated $14.5 million in 2014 compared to $357,613 in Shelter Cove. Port areas and ports differ in the species that dominate landings as well. In the Eureka port area, Dungeness crab landings accounted for more than half of the revenues from commercial fisheries. By contrast, in the Santa Barbara port area, market squid dominated, accounting for nearly half of the revenues. Landings of species such as market squid and Dungeness crab at individual ports can vary dramatically from year to year. In 2014, landings of Dungeness crab at Eureka generated $6.1 million at the dock, compared to $1.8 million in 2000. See Appendix F for more detail on landings at individual ports in 2014.

CALIFORNIA'S RECREATIONAL FISHERIES

Recreational fishing in California began soon after the Gold Rush. During the 1800s, sail-powered boats carried anglers to fish rockfish, Pacific halibut, salmon, and tuna. Commercial passenger fishing vessels (CPFVs) enabled anglers to access deep-sea fishing in the 1910s, and live-bait boats soon appeared in Southern California. From the 1800s through the early 1900s, recreational fishermen could catch surf perch, mackerel, white seabass, and even yellowtail from piers. California's population expansion in the mid-20th century led to a corresponding boom in marine recreational fishing, particularly in Southern California. During this period, angling evolved into a year-round activity, and technological innovations made recreational fishing more sophisticated and CPFVs more comfortable.

In 2011, the American Sportfishing Association ranked California fifth in the nation in total money spent by freshwater and saltwater anglers. A U.S. Fish and Wildlife Service survey from the same year reported 1,674,000 anglers in California, of which 775,000 were saltwater anglers. In total, saltwater anglers had almost 7.2 million fishing days in 2011. These statistics represent a decline over the preceding decade; in 2001, California had 2.4 million anglers including 932,000 saltwater fishers. The overall economic impact of recreational fishing, including both freshwater and saltwater angling, is greater than that of commercial fishing because of anglers' expenditures for goods and services such as transportation, fishing equipment, clothing, and boats. Saltwater recreational fisheries alone generated 12,134 jobs and over $1.7 billion in revenue in California in 2012, according to the *Fisheries Economics of the United States* report published by the National Oceanic and Atmospheric Administration (NOAA).

Recreational fishermen most commonly use rod and reel with artificial lures, live bait, or dead bait. Fishermen may also use hoop nets to catch crabs, lobsters, or shrimp. Divers catch a wide variety of finfish with spears, and may catch crabs, lobsters, abalone, urchins, and scallops by hand. Shore pickers gather mussels, clams, or crabs at low tide, or California grunion by moonlight. Rockfish, salmon, barracuda, bass, bonito, and several tuna species are all important recreational species in California. Data on California's recreational fisheries catch is recorded by the California Recreational Fisheries Survey (CRFS) and available online via the Recreational Fisheries Information Network (RecFIN), a division of the Pacific States Marine Fisheries Commission (PSMFC).

In 2012–2014, 31% of all fish landed or released recreationally were caught on charter or party boats, and another 39% by private or rental boats. (See Table 4.) The remainder was caught by anglers fishing on the beach (19%) or from man-made structures (11%). In 2015 the charter/party boat sector accounted for 56% of catch, while beach anglers caught just 2% of the total.

TABLE 4: RECREATIONAL CATCH BY YEAR AND MODE: 2004–2015

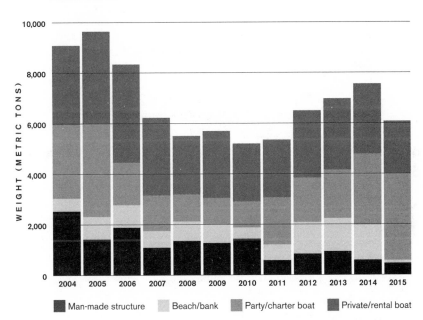

In 2014, 280 CPFVs operated in Southern California and 168 in Northern California. The most popular areas for party boat fishing are San Diego and Mission Bay (120 CPFVs), Seal Beach, Long Beach, and San Pedro (63 CPFVs), and San Francisco and San Francisco Bay Delta (74 CPFVs).

In 2014, approximately 2.2 million individual fish were landed in southern California, and just over 1 million in central and northern California. Sheephead, scorpionfish, Pacific bonito, kelp bass, yellowtail, tuna, and barracuda are almost exclusively caught in the south, while the north catches most of the striped bass, salmon, blue rockfish, and lingcod. Some species, such as California halibut, are popular with recreational fishers along the entire coast. Approximately ten percent of California recreational catch is from Mexican waters, where anglers primarily target dolphinfish, yellowtail, and bluefin and yellowfin tuna. Recreational red abalone catch from 2002 to 2012 was fairly consistent with an average annual take of 256,000 individuals; 96% of those came from Sonoma and Mendocino counties. Department report card data for the 2014–2015 fishing season estimates a recreational spiny lobster take of 215,295 individuals (approximately 344,472 pounds). The table below shows recreational take (both retained and released) of major recreational finfish in 2004 and 2014.

TABLE 5: NUMBERS OF FISH CAUGHT, RETAINED, OR RELEASED IN 2004 AND 2014 RECREATIONAL FISHERIES

SPECIES	2004 TOTAL TAKE, RETAINED AND RELEASED (MT)	2014 TOTAL TAKE, RETAINED AND RELEASED (MT)
Coho salmon	125.1	0.007
Chinook salmon	1215.1	25.1
Black rockfish	128.3	361.3
Blue rockfish	178.5	145.8
Bocaccio	70.0	102.5
CA scorpionfish	121.3	165.4
Lingcod	477.3	745.1
Kelp bass	549.1	496.5
Barred sandbass	732.5	121.6
Yellowtail	452.3	607.1
White seabass	122.6	63.8
Barred surfperch	167.3	272.4
Pacific barracuda	821.6	118.3
Skipjack tuna	46.7	18.6
Pacific bonito	744.0	206.1
Chub mackerel	1105.0	285.4
Albacore	261.3	0.9
Bluefin tuna	0.8	59.5
Yellowfin tuna	17.1	350.5
CA halibut	377.1	232.6

CALIFORNIA'S CHANGING FISHERIES

Marine fisheries in California have changed dramatically since passage of the MLMA as governmental programs and regulations, economic conditions, markets, technology, and other factors have evolved in the past 17 years. Consider the following:

- Since 2000, invertebrate fisheries, particularly for market squid and Dungeness crab, have grown from just over half to as much as three-quarters of the value of all commercial landings.

- While the total volume of landings fell from 553 million pounds in 2000 to 358 million pounds in 2014, the nominal value of landings rose from $136 million to $235 million. The increase in nominal revenue to fishermen at the dock was driven by increases in landings of market squid and Dungeness crab, and in prices for spiny lobster, sea cucumber, and rock crab, in particular.

- Operating costs for fishing have increased. For example, monthly retail prices for diesel fuel rose from $1.07–$1.55 per gallon in 2000 to $2.60–$3.11 in 2015, according to the Pacific States Marine Fisheries Commission (PSMFC).

- In 2000, the entire West Coast groundfish fishery was declared a fishery failure; soon afterwards, hundreds of square miles of ocean waters were closed and remain closed in order to protect overfished species. The groundfish fleet was reduced in size through a buy-out and implementation of a quota share program. Some species of concern have recovered.

- In late 2013, warm water began expanding along the west coast from Alaska to Baja, raising surface water temperatures to unprecedented high levels and reducing the upwelling of nutrient-rich bottom waters that drive ocean productivity. The impact of these changes rippled through ocean ecosystems off the west coast, leading to massive die-offs of marine mammals and seabirds as forage populations declined, for example. The warm water "blob" was broken up in late 2015 by a major El Nino event. Never has the North Pacific Ocean been so warm for so long since records began being kept.

- In 2015–2016, northern California kelp forests were reduced by more than 90% to an all-time low by unprecedented changes in ocean temperature and chemistry, the decimation of sea stars by a wasting disease, reducing predation on kelp-consuming sea urchins.

- In 2015, a harmful algal bloom spanned much of the West Coast, leading to high levels of domoic acid in nearshore waters and the contamination of shellfish, in particular. For public health reasons, California did not open the commercial and recreational Dungeness crab fisheries until March 2016—by far the latest opening in history.
- In 1992, 80% of recreational fishers targeting spiny lobsters were divers, and 20% used boat-based hoop nets; those percentages flipped as of 2007. Recreational lobster take in 2014–2015 accounted for approximately 26% of the total spiny lobster catch, contributing $33–$40 million to the California economy.
- Recreational take of salmon—historically one of the most active recreational fisheries in the state—plummeted in 2008–2009 due to a decline in coho and a collapse in the Chinook populations leading to statewide fishery closures. The fishery has not rebounded to the levels seen a decade ago. In 2004, recreational anglers took about 125 metric tons of coho and 1,215 of Chinook; in 2014, they caught almost no coho and just 25 metric tons of Chinook, due to reduced quotas reflecting extraordinarily low returns of adult salmon in previous years.
- In 2012, the state completed a network of 124 marine protected areas along the California coast, covering 16.5% of California's ocean, including 9.4% in no-take areas.
- Since 1999, the demand for seafood from sustainable sources has grown among consumers in the United States and abroad, and with that demand, programs for evaluation of the sustainability of fisheries by third-party organizations has also increased.

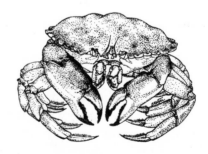

— CHAPTER 2 —
THE MANAGEMENT SETTING

THE MANAGEMENT OF marine living resources off California is a mosaic of international, federal, and state law and governing agencies. Generally, waters from the shoreline to three miles are state waters; from three miles to 200 miles is the U.S. Exclusive Economic Zone (EEZ) or federal waters; and beyond 200 miles are international waters or "high seas." However, as the matrix in Appendix B illustrates, the division of management authority among international, federal, and state jurisdictions is often complex. In essence, the state is responsible for managing any species that is caught in state waters or landed in the state but is not included in a federal fishery management plan. For example, nearshore species such as spiny lobster and sheephead are entirely under the jurisdiction of California. Species that occur principally in federal waters such as swordfish, deep water groundfish, and sardines are managed by the federal government. Species such as tuna that occur principally on the high seas are primarily managed under international treaty.

Marine life is not restricted by artificial designations, and populations frequently straddle or move across international borders and management boundaries. For instance, bluefin tuna caught in United States waters migrate thousands of miles across the Pacific Ocean at certain stages in their lives. Because fishing for a species that moves between any of these boundaries may involve all governmental organizations with jurisdiction, coordinated management is critical for fishers and managers.

The following description of these management jurisdictions and their overlap is not exhaustive, but seeks to provide a basic orientation and includes the information most relevant to the MLMA. More detailed information on state policies and management in particular is the focus of Chapter 3.

INTERNATIONAL MANAGEMENT

Beyond 200 miles from shore lie the high seas, where any management of activities affecting marine wildlife is left to treaties among countries. Regional Fishery Management Organizations or RFMOs, composed of delegates from countries that border or fish in that region, draft and oversee these international agreements. For example, the Inter-American Tropical Tuna Commission (IATTC) makes recommendations for the management of fishing on tuna and tuna-like species on the high seas in the Eastern Pacific Ocean. Specialized international organizations also exist to manage particular species that are not highly migratory, but do straddle international boundaries. For example, since 1923, the management of Pacific halibut has been guided by the International Pacific Halibut Commission (IPHC), which was established by Canada and the United States.

Like other member countries, the United States sends delegations to meetings of these international organizations; these delegations are composed of representatives of the State Department, NOAA Fisheries, and depending upon the international organization, presidentially appointed commissioners, and advisory committee members. Generally, NOAA Fisheries is responsible for promulgating and implementing any regulations required by decisions taken by these organizations. In some cases, the Pacific Fishery Management Council (PFMC) described below, the states, and stakeholder advisory bodies play a role in shaping U.S. positions and implementation of management decisions. For example, the PFMC consults with its stakeholders and recommends Pacific halibut harvest regulations to the IPHC, and allocates catches to commercial, tribal, and sport fisheries, which the states then implement. NOAA Fisheries and the PFMC also have the authority to make management decisions that go above and beyond what is set forth by a RFMO, such as more stringent bycatch caps or reduced quotas for tuna species.

FEDERAL MANAGEMENT

The federal agency with primary responsibility for the conservation and management of marine fisheries is NOAA Fisheries, an agency of the National Oceanic and Atmospheric Administration in the U.S. Department of Commerce. The principal federal fisheries management law is the Magnuson-Stevens Fishery Conservation and Management Act (MSA), which was signed into law in 1976, and most recently reauthorized in 2006 with amendments focused on fisheries sustainability. The MSA established eight regional fishery management councils, composed of fishermen, others in the seafood industry, public interest groups, and state and federal fisheries managers. These councils have lead responsibility for developing and amending fishery management plans (FMPs) for fisheries in their regions, guided by the MSA's National Standards and assisted by NOAA Fisheries. Councils also routinely develop management recommendations to implement the FMPs on a continuing basis, such as setting Annual Catch Limits (ACLs), updating gear and area restrictions, addressing allocation issues, etc. FMPs developed by the councils are reviewed for their consistency with the National Standards by NOAA Fisheries, which also promulgates and enforces accompanying regulations.

Pacific Fishery Management Council

On the West Coast, the federal fishery management process begins with the Pacific Fishery Management Council, or PFMC. The PFMC consists of 14 voting members, including one representative from the management agencies of California, Oregon, Washington, and Idaho (given the state's salmon populations), one obligatory member from each state, four at-large members, one tribal representative and one NOAA Fisheries representative. The Secretary of Commerce appoints the obligatory and at-large representatives from a pool of nominees submitted by each governor. Some members are appointed by their respective agencies. The council also includes five non-voting members, such as representatives of the U.S. Fish & Wildlife Service and the U.S. Coast Guard. Fisheries within the 200-mile Exclusive Economic Zone (EEZ) may be managed under fishery management plans developed by the PFMC and approved by the Secretary of Commerce.

The PFMC's deliberations are informed by a number of advisory bodies. The Magnuson-Stevens Act requires establishment of a Science and Statistical Committee (SSC), a group of scientists from government agencies, academic institutions, and other organizations. The SSC reviews FMPs, stock assessments, rebuilding plans, and other documents to ensure that decisions are based on the best available science. Under the 2006 amendments to the Magnuson-Stevens Act, the SSC gained the responsibility for setting the initial biological target for management of a fishery; previously, an SSC would provide a range of estimates for a target, from which a council would then select. The PFMC is also supported by plan development, enforcement, technical, and management teams, composed of state, federal, tribal, and non-governmental scientific specialists, who provide data and analyses on specific fisheries. Members of the panels are selected by the PFMC members and serve three-year terms. Finally, the PFMC has established a number of advisory panels primarily composed of representatives from the fishing industry, on salmon, groundfish, coastal pelagic species, highly migratory species, habitat, and ecosystems. The Habitat Committee, for example, evaluates essential fish habitat in FMPs, advises on the impact of proposed management measures on habitat, and reviews activities authorized, funded, or undertaken by federal or state agencies that may affect habitat of a fishery under council jurisdiction.

Over the years, the PFMC has adopted and amended FMPs for the following fisheries: groundfish, highly migratory species, salmon, and coastal pelagic species. The PFMC has also adopted a Fishery Ecosystem Plan. California fishers engage in each of these fisheries to some extent, and each plan is described in Appendix E. These FMPs are implemented by NOAA Fisheries.

Pacific States Marine Fisheries Commission

Together with Alaska, Idaho, Oregon, and Washington, California is a member of the PSMFC. The PSMFC, which was established by Congress through an interstate compact in 1947, has no regulatory powers, but aims at promoting coordinated management of fisheries in state waters. Among other things, the PSMFC manages basic data on commercial and recreational fisheries submitted by the individual states, available through two public databases: the Pacific Fisheries Information Network (PacFIN) for commercial fisheries and RecFIN for recreational fisheries. The PSMFC is also home for the Tri-State Dungeness Crab Committee, through which California, Oregon, and Washington coordinate management of the fishery.

Federally Protected Species

Several other federal laws guide the management of marine life off California. NOAA Fisheries shares responsibility with the Interior Department's U.S. Fish and Wildlife Service for species under the Endangered Species Act (ESA) and the Marine Mammal Protection Act (MMPA). While the

U.S. Fish and Wildlife Service holds responsibility for the conservation of southern sea otters and birds, NOAA Fisheries oversees the conservation of protected fish and shellfish, seals, sea lions, dolphins, and whales off California.

Several species of marine life have been listed under the Endangered Species Act of 1973, which prohibits "taking" (defined as "to pursue, hunt, shoot, capture, collect, kill or attempt") of an endangered species. Limited taking of an endangered species incidental to activities such as fishing may be permitted. These and other protections for endangered species do not apply to threatened species unless separate regulations are adopted. Under Section 7 of the Endangered Species Act, federal agencies must consult with NOAA Fisheries or the U.S. Fish and Wildlife Service to ensure that their actions do not jeopardize the continued existence of listed species.

The following species and populations found along California's coast have been listed as endangered under the federal Endangered Species Act: humpback, blue, fin, sei, and sperm whales; leatherback, olive ridley, green, and hawksbill sea turtles; Sacramento winter-run chinook salmon; southern California steelhead; and California least tern. Threatened species include Central Valley spring-run chinook, California coastal chinook, and Central and Northern California coho salmon; steelhead of the Central Valley and the south-central and northern California coasts; southern sea otters; Guadalupe fur seals; loggerhead sea turtles; marbled murrelets; and snowy plovers.

The Marine Mammal Protection Act (MMPA) of 1972 imposed a moratorium on "taking" marine mammals, with a few exceptions that include taking marine mammals incidental to commercial fishing. Under the MMPA, taking may include intentional or unintentional capture or harassment. Amendments to the MMPA adopted by Congress in 1994 established a new regime to govern incidental taking in commercial fishing. This program aims to reduce serious injury and mortality of marine mammals to insignificant levels approaching a zero rate. The regime divides fisheries into three categories, based on criteria such as the frequency of marine mammal captures and the degree of threat that the capture poses to marine mammal populations. Vessels in Categories I or II must register with NOAA Fisheries and may be required to carry an observer to collect information. Of California fisheries, the drift gillnet fishery for thresher shark and swordfish is in Category I, according to NOAA Fisheries 2017

List of Fisheries. Category II fisheries are the set gillnet fishery for California halibut and white seabass, the drift gillnet fishery for yellowtail, barracuda, and white seabass, the pot fishery for spot prawns, the pot fishery for Dungeness crab, and the pot fishery for sablefish.

The Pacific Offshore Cetacean Take Reduction Team, composed of fishermen, scientists, and conservationists, was convened by NOAA Fisheries to suggest means of reducing the incidental catch of marine mammals in the swordfish drift gillnet fishery off California. In 1997, NOAA Fisheries adopted regulations requiring that fishermen use pingers on their nets, which emit sounds to alert marine mammals, and hang their nets well below the surface in order to reduce the capture of several species of small whales as well as humpback and sperm whales.

The Migratory Bird Treaty Act implements several international treaties, and stipulates that migratory birds may not be captured or killed unless permitted by regulations adopted by the Secretary of the Interior. Seabirds, shorebirds, and other nongame birds fall under the protection of the Migratory Bird Treaty Act.

STATE MANAGEMENT

The policies and approaches that make up California state fisheries management are the focus of this book and are discussed in detail in Chapter 3. However, an overview of the underlying authorities, management bodies, and funding sources is provided here.

State Jurisdiction

The federal Submerged Lands Act of 1953 granted and confirmed to the State of California concurrent jurisdiction over the control and regulation of marine resources, including marine living resources as well as oil and gas and other minerals, in state waters within three miles of the shoreline—an area of 5,767 square statute miles. There are several exceptions to this general rule. For instance, under the MMPA and the ESA, the federal government has pre-empted state authority in the conservation of marine mammals and endangered and threatened species in state waters.

California can regulate vessels licensed in California wherever they fish. It can also regulate fishermen licensed in other states whenever they fish in California state waters or land their catch in California ports. Absent congressional authority, if vessels from other states fish beyond three miles offshore and do not call at a California port, the state cannot control their activities. Similarly, the states of Oregon and Washington do not have jurisdiction over California vessels that fish in waters more than three miles off their shores, e.g., for pink shrimp and Dungeness crab, and land their catch in California.

State regulations must be consistent with federal regulations for species included in a federal fishery management plan. Generally, that means that state regulation may be stricter but not less restrictive than the federal requirements. As described below, depending upon the species, management may involve the Legislature, the Fish and Game Commission, and/or the California Department of Fish and Wildlife.

California Legislature

The California legislature consists of a Senate and an Assembly, and passage by both houses is required before a bill moves to the Governor for signature. The Senate has 40 members and the Assembly has 80. On the Assembly side, the Water, Parks, and Wildlife Committee and the Assembly Appropriations Committee are most engaged in fisheries related issues. On the Senate side, the Natural Resource and Water Committee and the Senate Appropriations Committee have jurisdiction over most laws affecting ocean fisheries. The Joint Committee on Fisheries and Aquaculture, which was formed in 1981, reviews, analyzes, and makes legislative and other recommendations regarding fisheries and aquaculture in the state.

While bills must have a member of the legislature as an author, they often also have interest group "sponsors" which may have brought the issue to the attention of the author. Sponsors and their lobbyists are often engaged in advocating for the bill and addressing any concerns as it moves forward. As legislation moves forward through these committees and to the floor, it may be amended many times to address the concerns of members, various stakeholder groups, and agencies.

The legislature has delegated considerable authority for management of commercial fisheries to the Commission, particularly with the passage of the MLMA. However, that authority has often been guided by the broad policies and specific requirements set forth in laws such as the MLMA and by the constitutional requirement of separation of powers. The legislature has also retained specific aspects of management such as landing tax rates, and some species-specific authorities relating to gear restrictions, permitting conditions, and spatial management. In some cases, the retention of authority by the Legislature is deliberate and by design, such as with the commercial Dungeness crab fishery. In other cases it is more a function of historical evolution. The table in Appendix B describes in detail the division of authority among the various management entities for select West Coast species.

California Fish and Game Commission

Article IV, Section 20 of the California Constitution created the Fish and Game Commission, which began in 1870 as the Board of Fish Commissioners. The Commission has five members, who are private citizens, not state employees. There are no requirements in the California Constitution that a commissioner represent a specific constituency or geographic area, or have a specific background or expertise. However, the legislature encourages the selection of candidates who add diversity, have knowledge of wildlife and natural resources management and science, and are familiar with public policy decision-making. Commissioners in California are appointed to staggered six year terms by the governor. By staggering the terms, a new governor or legislature cannot suddenly change the makeup of the Commission for political reasons. A commissioner is allowed to serve up to one year before his/her confirmation by the Senate, and may continue to serve beyond his/her term until the governor nominates a replacement.

As originally conceived, the Commission regulated recreational activities as they related to natural resources while the legislature retained jurisdiction over commercial fishing. However, over time the legislature has delegated much but not all jurisdiction over commercial fisheries to the Commission. A general responsibility of the Commission is to afford an opportunity for full public input and participation in the decision-making process. Specific Commission responsibilities include:
- formulation of general policies for the conduct of the Department
- seasons, bag limits and methods of take (i.e. gear restrictions) for hunting, sport fishing, and some commercial fishing
- controlling non-native species' importation, possession, and sale
- establishing protected lands/waters (ecological reserves and marine managed areas, of which marine protected areas are one type)
- regulating uses of protected areas

- listing threatened/endangered species under the California Endangered Species Act
- leasing State water-bottom for shellfish cultivation
- leasing State water columns for finfish mariculture
- leasing kelp beds for harvest
- considering appeal hearings for revocation or suspension of licenses and permits
- prescribing terms and conditions for issuance, suspension, revocation of licenses/permits issued by the Department
- implementing emergency fishery closures when necessary due to changing environmental conditions or sudden population declines

The Commission has developed a set of general policies that guide its decision-making. All Commission policies can be viewed at www.fgc.ca.gov/policy/ and those most directly related to marine fisheries are listed below:

- tribal Consultation, adopted June 10, 2015
- forage Species, adopted November 7, 2012
- marine Protected Areas, amended December 9, 2015
- emerging Fisheries, adopted October 20, 2000
- restricted Access Commercial Fisheries, adopted June 18, 1999
- shellfish and Sea Otter Conflicts, adopted April 1, 1999

Currently the Commission has three sub-committees: the Marine Resources Committee (MRC) and Wildlife Resources Committee (WRC), which were created in statute (Sections 105 and 106 of the Fish and Game Code), and the Tribal Committee. Each is typically chaired or co-chaired by two commissioners. A goal of these committees is to allow more informal discussions on issues and regulatory proposals than what is possible at full Commission meetings. The committee meetings are less structured in nature and provide for additional access to the Commission.

On average, the Commission meets in person six times per year in locations across the state, and additionally holds teleconference meetings for individual issues as needed. The Commission is staffed by a small team of state employees including a marine advisor. While the Commission is distinct from the Department, it is funded as a line item in the Department's budget.

The Commission's scope is broad. In 2015 and 2016, for example, the Commission addressed a wide range of issues including:

- continuing the process of phasing out lead ammunition, as directed by the legislature, and authorizing a non-lead ammunition coupon program to encourage the transition
- adopting an emergency reduction in abalone take to address degrading environmental ocean conditions and declining abalone populations
- adopting regulations to enhance penalties for the illegal take of game to further deter poaching
- designating new lake and river segments as Wild Trout Waters and Heritage Trout Waters to help improve angler access and opportunities in lakes and streams where native trout reside
- holding the first of a series of fishing communities meetings designed to identify common and specific challenges to California's commercial fisheries along the coast in a changing ocean climate
- adopting regulations concerning the allowance of tribal privileges for ceremonial and subsistence harvest for Redding rock SMCA along the northern California coast
- developing a policy resolution focused on the impacts of climate change on California's fish and wildlife resources, to be advanced through the wildlife, marine, and tribal committees to help ensure that the goals of the state's wildlife action plan and California's climate adaptation strategy are met

California Department of Fish and Wildlife

Established within the California Natural Resources Agency, the Department manages and protects the state's fish, wildlife and native habitats while overseeing their recreational, commercial, scientific and educational use. The Department is a public trustee of fish and wildlife resources and has jurisdiction over the conservation, protection, and management of fish, wildlife, native plants, and habitats necessary for biologically sustainable populations of those species. The Department's director and chief deputy director are appointed by the governor and confirmed by the legislature.

Administratively, the state is broken up into seven "regions" including the Marine Region, described below. There are also a number of distinct Department divisions outside of the regions dedicated to functions including enforcement, wildlife and fisheries, legislative affairs, licensing, and oil spill response. In addition to implementing policies formulated by the legislature and the Commission, the Department also manages its own programs and sets its own policies on conservation, law enforcement, commercial and recreational fishing, spill response and public lands. The Department also collects biological data that the Commission uses in its decision-making.

The Marine Region, which was established as a function within the Department in November 1997, encompasses the entire California coastline from the shoreline to three nautical miles out to sea, including waters around offshore islands, covering approximately 5,767 square statute miles of ocean and bay waters. The Marine Region's activities are organized under five programs. Fourteen projects are housed within the five programs:

- aquaculture and bay management
- Northern and Central California finfish research and management
- Southern California fisheries research and management
- coastal pelagic species and highly migratory species
- groundfish
- invertebrate management
- ocean salmon
- Marine Fisheries Statistical Unit
- recreational fisheries data
- marine protected areas
- Marine Region administration and license sales
- project review/water quality
- research vessel operations
- diving safety

In 2015 the Marine Region issued a profile of its activities and accomplishments, which provides a better sense of the scope and scale of the Marine Region's activities. In 2015, the Marine Region:

- Contacted more than 58,000 saltwater angling parties, identified more than 222,000 fish and invertebrates, and measured more than 126,000 fish;
- Entered more than 56,000 commercial landing receipts;
- Reviewed 681 environmental documents, and submitted more than 70 comment letters and permits;

- Submitted nine regulatory packages to the Fish and Game Commission;
- Issued 172 Scientific Collecting Permits;
- Reviewed and approved 175 aquaculture registration permits;
- Distributed more than 27,000 MPA guidebooks and 31,000 MPA brochures;
- Completed 76 kilometers of transects with a remotely operated vehicle from 24 sites inside and outside MPAs off the north central coast.

Since passage of the MLMA in 1998, the Marine Region has prepared fishery management plans, adopted by the Fish and Game Commission, for the white seabass fishery, the nearshore finfish fishery, the market squid fishery, and the spiny lobster fishery. Under separate legislation, the Marine Region prepared an abalone recovery and management plan, and, in 2015, began preparing a red abalone fishery management plan consistent with the MLMA. The Marine Region also is responsible for the state's role in federal management of certain fisheries under the MSA, including coastal pelagic species, groundfish, highly migratory species, Pacific halibut, salmon, and ecosystem-based management.

Funding of State Fisheries Management Efforts

Department Funding

Over the years, the Department's and Commission's budgets have varied widely in response to changes in general governmental revenues, in revenues from Department-related fees, and in programs and mandates. For fiscal year 2017–2018, the Governor proposed a budget of approximately $523 million for the Department, of which roughly $14 million is allocated to commercial fisheries management and $46 million is allocated to sport fishing management (both marine and freshwater). The revenues supporting the overall Department budget come from four main sources:

- Fish and Game Preservation Fund, 23%
- General Fund, 17%
- Federal Trust Fund, 15%
- Bond funds, 12%, and
- The remaining 33% from reimbursements and other small funds

The Fish and Game Preservation Fund (FGPF) is divided into 29 dedicated accounts, for which revenues can be spent only on activities linked to the source of the revenue, such as the Duck Stamp Account, and a non-dedicated account, for which revenues can be spent on a variety of the Department's activities. Sportfishing licenses and permits account for approximately 65% of the Fish and Game Preservation Fund, hunting licenses approximately 23%, commercial fishing licenses and permits approximately 3%, and commercial landings taxes about one percent. The balance of the fund is derived from other sources, such as license plate fees and other regulatory fees. This fund has been steadily depleted in recent years as expenditures have exceeded revenues.

The largest expenditure of non-dedicated FGPF funds is law enforcement. This account also supports management of Department owned lands, inland and coastal fisheries, commercial fisheries management, departmental review of activities under the California Environmental Quality Act, and such other efforts as projects aimed at restoring salmon and steelhead trout runs.

General funds, which are appropriated by the legislature from state tax revenues, can vary dramatically from year to year, with fluctuations in the economy and changing priorities. Federal trust funds represent federal grants, such as those under the Sport Fish Restoration Program that funds restoration and management of fisheries; the program is funded by federal excise taxes on fishing equipment, motorboat and small engine fuels, and import duties. Finally, nearly half of the Department's revenues come from a variety of sources, some of which are dedicated to particular purposes and are unavailable for supporting other Department operations.

Section 711 of the Fish and Game Code specifies that the costs of commercial fishing programs should be covered by the revenues from commercial fishing taxes, license fees, and other revenues, as well as other funds appropriated by the legislature. Similarly, recreational fishing programs are to be supported by revenues from permits and other sources, including appropriations by the legislature. In 2016, the state collected more than $65 million from sport fishing licenses, validations, and report cards. In the same year, the state collected $3.8 million from commercial license fees and $1.4 million from commercial landings taxes.

According to a 2017 report by the California Legislative Analyst's Office (LAO), commercial fishing permit fees and landings taxes generated roughly $5 million in funding in 2015–16, when the Department expended more than $20 million in managing commercial fisheries. According to the LAO, the gap was closed, as in past years, with funding largely from recreational hunting and fishing license fees.

Structural and other problems in the Department's budget extend beyond ocean fisheries. Despite periodic intense discussions between different governors and legislatures over the last couple of decades, these problems have persisted.

Non-Department Government Funding

Outside the Department budget itself are a variety of public funding sources that support fisheries-related projects proposed by stakeholders or agencies. Some of these sources and opportunities are described below:

Ocean Protection Council: Since 2004, the OPC has helped to provide funding to advance fisheries management and other state priorities. The OPC was established by the California Ocean Protection Act and is made up of seven members of state government and the public. Among other things, the OPC directs bond and other funds towards a wide range of projects targeted at improving ocean health. OPC's specific funding priorities are shaped in consultation with state agencies and with input from the public.

Since 2005, OPC has provided $84 million in funding for around 150 projects, from $2,500 for Sea Otter Recovery Research to $5.7 million for Statewide Science Integration and Marine Protected Area Monitoring. In 2008, the OPC authorized the distribution of $300,000 to create a collaborative fisheries research (CFR) organization in California called CFR West. OPC also provided funding to establish the California Fisheries Fund, to modernize Department data collection and management, and to develop guidance on taking climate change into account in fisheries management.

Sea Grant: The National Sea Grant Program was established by Congress in 1966 to "unite the academic power of the nation's universities with public and private sector partners in order to capture the economic and social benefits of the oceans, coasts and Great Lakes in a sustainable manner." The California Sea Grant College program was established in 1973 and is one of 33 NOAA funded state programs. It is administered by the Scripps

Institution of Oceanography at the University of California San Diego. It offers:

- Grant and fellowship opportunities for scientists and graduate students
- Complete proposals solicitation, review, and grant administration services
- Extension specialists dedicated to impartial research and outreach for coastal stakeholders and communities
- Connection to a nation-wide network of Sea Grant experts and partners

California Sea Grant funds approximately 60 projects per year with research proposals typically solicited in late January. The University of Southern California also supports a Sea Grant Program that focuses upon the heavily used ocean waters off urban areas such as Los Angeles.

Sport Fish Restoration Act: The Sport Fish Restoration Program (SFR) provides grant funds to the states and the District of Columbia for fishery projects, boating access, and aquatic education. SFR is authorized by the Sport Fish Restoration Act of 1950 and was created to restore and better manage "America's declining fishery resources." Excise taxes on fishing equipment, motorboat and small engine fuels, import duties, and interest are collected and appropriated from the Sport Fish Restoration and Boating Trust Fund. These funds are apportioned to states based on a formula which includes land area, number of paid license holders, minimums and maximums. Grant funds are disbursed to states for approved grants up to 75% of the project costs. Over the past half century, this program has generated more than $2.6 billion, which has been used to support research, hatchery construction, public education, and the construction and maintenance of thousands of fishing and boating access sites. In California, the SFR helps fund programs like the Ocean Resources Enhancement and Hatchery Program and the Fishing in the City Program.

Saltonstall-Kennedy Grant Program: The Saltonstall-Kennedy Act established a program funded by a share of import fees on seafood to provide grants for fisheries research and projects geared towards enhancing U.S. fisheries, including harvesting, processing, marketing and associated business infrastructures. A primary focus of the program, which is managed by NOAA, is to support efforts by fisheries and fishing communities to optimize economic benefits from sustainable fisheries. In 2015, NOAA awarded Saltonstall-Kennedy grants to 88 projects, totaling $25 million of support. These grants spanned the U.S. coasts, and included many projects relevant to California, including one to test electronic monitoring for the drift gillnet swordfish fishery, and another to explore artificial reefs as tools to aid the recovery of protected species. Requests for proposals are generally issued annually and applications are generally due in the fall.

Bycatch Reduction Engineering Program: In addition to the Saltonstall-Kennedy grant program, NOAA also administers the Bycatch Reduction Engineering Program (BREP), which supports engineering and gear modification projects intended to reduce bycatch and post-release mortality in federally managed fisheries. In 2015, BREP provided $2.5 million to fishermen, academics, and other interested groups for projects that presented practical technological and engineering bycatch reduction solutions. Past projects have included the development of a new circle hook that reduces bluefin tuna bycatch by 56% as well as the testing of new fishing gear to reduce the bycatch of Columbia River smelt in the pink shrimp trawl fishery by 90%.

Coastal Impact Assistance Program: The Department of the Interior administrates the Coastal Impact Assistance Program (CIAP), which uses funds from offshore oil and gas leases to assist states where offshore drilling occurs. CIAP funds must be used to restore, enhance, and protect renewable natural resources. In California, the Natural Resources Agency is responsible for implementing the CIAP, and has funded a number of projects and programs relevant to California fisheries, including ecosystem-based monitoring, research to support the MLPA and MLMA, and enhanced marine law enforcement.

Industry Funding

The fishing industry identifies and funds priority projects that promote sustainable seafood and economically healthy fisheries. Fishermen and processors, working both together and separately, have funded a wide range of science and economic improvement efforts. Several examples are provided below:

The California Sea Urchin Commission: The California Sea Urchin Commission (CSUC) was created in 2004 with the support of participants in the fishery and represents the interests of California's nearly 300 licensed sea urchin divers. The Commission operates under state law to ensure a sustainable sea urchin resource by supporting strong local coastal communities and fishermen engaged in sea urchin commercial fishing through various industry initiatives. The Commission's activities are funded by an assessment on sea urchin harvested and processed in California.

The California Wetfish Producers Association: The California Wetfish Producers Association (CWPA) is an association of harvesters and processors that was established in 2004 to promote sustainable sardine, mackerel, anchovy, market squid, and coastal tuna fisheries. The CWPA has sponsored cooperative research with the Department and NOAA Fisheries Southwest Fishery Science Center to create an improved understanding of the status of various coastal pelagic stocks.

Sea Pact: The processing and distribution sector has also come together to make funding available to others for projects that promote sustainable fisheries. Sea Pact is an alliance formed among nine North American seafood distributors with the goal of advancing environmentally sustainable fisheries and aquaculture practices. Since its inception in 2014, Sea Pact has provided grants to fisheries and aquaculture improvements all over the world, including California. Grants have totaled more than $137,000. In 2015, Sea Pact placed an emphasis on projects that focus efforts on reducing bycatch, developing innovations for aquaculture, and increasing social responsibility within the seafood supply chain.

Sportfishing Association of California: The Sportfishing Association of California (SAC) has helped fund surveys of sportfish such as bluefin tuna. SAC and other recreational fishing groups have worked cooperatively with state and federal fishery managers to enhance understanding of the status of the state's sportfish populations. The group's funding is derived from member dues and donations. See: http://www.californiasportfishing.org/.

TRIBAL MANAGEMENT AND ENGAGEMENT

Native American tribes have been managing and harvesting fisheries for millennia along the California coast. The United States Government recognizes some Native American tribes as separate and independent political communities. These tribes have a trust relationship with the U.S. Government and interact with it on a government-to-government basis.

In 2011, Governor Edmund G. Brown, Jr. issued Executive Order B-10-11 to "implement effective government-to-government consultation" with federally recognized tribes and those on the contact list maintained by the Native American Heritage Commission. In November 2012, the California Natural Resources Agency adopted a Tribal Consultation Policy pursuant to the Executive Order. In October 2014, the Department adopted a detailed policy to provide a foundation "to work cooperatively, communicate effectively, and consult with tribes." Finally, in June 2015, the Commission adopted a Tribal Consultation Policy, which emphasizes communication and collaboration and commits to maintaining a record of all comments provided by tribes and to training regarding Commission regulatory and policy development.

The Department's policy establishes a formal process for the Department to engage in government-to-government consultation with tribes. The Department seeks to engage with tribes as early as possible in the decision-making process in order to properly understand the potential impacts of state management of fisheries on Native American Tribes within the state. The policy recognizes that many of the Department's proposed activities and fisheries management efforts may significantly impact the interests of tribes. The policy commits the Department to consulting with tribes about fishery management issues, assessing and avoiding to the extent practicable any potential impact of Department activities on tribal interests, and providing tribes with meaningful opportunities to participate in decision-making processes that affect tribal interests.

The state has sought to minimize and avoid impacts to tribal interests in inland and marine fisheries. Regarding marine fisheries, for example, the Fish and Game Commission has exempted certain tribes from the area and take restrictions of specific north-coast marine protected areas in which the tribe has a demonstrated historical use of marine resources. However, tribal members are required to observe general bag, possession, and size limits and to possess a valid tribal identification and any necessary

Department report cards or licenses. Free fishing licenses are available to tribal members with low annual income.

Certain tribes have established their own fisheries management entities. The work of tribes throughout the state has greatly benefitted the understanding and management of California's marine resources. The Department, NOAA Fisheries, and California universities also collaborate with and fund tribal research in order to more effectively monitor marine resources.

— CHAPTER 3 —

THE MARINE LIFE MANAGEMENT ACT

THE MARINE LIFE MANAGEMENT ACT, which became law on January 1, 1999, opened a new era in the management and conservation of marine living resources in California. In fashioning the MLMA, which had been introduced as AB 1241 by Assemblyman Fred Keeley in February 1997, the Legislature drew upon years of experience in California and elsewhere in the United States and the world.

The Act includes a number of innovative features. First, the MLMA applies not only to fish and shellfish taken by commercial and recreational fishermen, but to all marine wildlife under state jurisdiction. Second, rather than assuming that exploitation should continue until damage has become clear, the MLMA was intended to shift the burden of proof toward demonstrating that fisheries and other activities are sustainable. Third, while the Legislature retained its control of some of the State's commercial fisheries, it gave the Commission new authority, using the standards and procedures of the MLMA.

The MLMA sets out several underlying goals:

- Conserve Entire Systems: It is not simply exploited populations of marine life that are to be conserved, but the species and habitats that make up the ecosystem of which they are a part [7050(b)1].
- Non-Consumptive Values: Marine life need not be consumed to provide important benefits to people, including aesthetic and recreational enjoyment as well as scientific study and education [7050(a)].
- Sustainability: Fisheries and other uses of marine living resources are to be sustainable so that long-term health is not sacrificed for short-term benefits [7055(a); 7050(b)2].

- Habitat Conservation: The habitat of marine wildlife is to be maintained, restored or enhanced, and any damage from fishing practices is to be minimized [7055(b); 7056(b)].
- Restoration: Depressed fisheries are to be rebuilt quickly within a specified time that accounts for the biology of the stock and environmental conditions [7055(b); 7056(c), 7086(c)1].
- Bycatch: The bycatch of marine living resources in fisheries is to be limited to acceptable types and amounts [7056(d)].
- Fishing Communities: Fisheries management should recognize the long-term interests of people dependent on fishing, and adverse impacts of management measures on fishing communities are to be minimized [7056(i and j)].

To meet these policy objectives, the MLMA calls for using several basic tools:

- Science: Management is to be based on the best available scientific information as well as other relevant information. Lack of information should not greatly delay taking action. To help ensure the scientific soundness of decisions, key documents should be reviewed by experts [7050(b)6; 7062; 7072(b)].
- Constituent Involvement: The MLMA calls for decision making that is open and that involves people who are interested in or affected by management measures [7056(h)].
- Fishery Management Plans: Rather than *ad hoc* and piecemeal decisions on individual fisheries, the MLMA calls for basing decisions on comprehensive reviews of fisheries and on clear objectives and measures for fostering sustainable fisheries. The vehicle for this effort is a fishery management plan [7070; 7078].
- Master Plan: The Department will prepare, and the Commission will adopt, a Master Plan that prioritizes fisheries according to need for changes in management in order to comply with the policies of the MLMA [7073]. The Master Plan is intended to undergo periodic review and amendment.
- Status of the Fisheries Report: Annually, the Department will prepare a report on the status of California's fisheries and the effectiveness of management programs [7065; 7066].

OVERALL POLICIES

Below is a description of the Marine Life Management Act's many sections. This description reorganizes the MLMA's provisions into five broad categories that move from general statements of policy to application of the policy. These categories are:

- general policies
- scope
- general means for achieving the MLMA's goals
- specific tools
- socio-economic considerations

Where the text of this guide is based directly on a provision of the MLMA, a citation is provided in brackets. As with any description of legislation, this guide is somewhat interpretive. The full text of the MLMA, as amended and as it appears in the Fish and Game Code, may be found in Appendix A.

Definitions of key terms may also be found at the beginning of Appendix A as well. These terms include adaptive management, bycatch, depressed fishery, discards, emerging fishery, essential fishery information, fish, fishery, limited entry fishery, marine living resources, maximum sustainable yield, nearshore fish stocks, nearshore fisheries, nearshore waters, optimum yield, overfished, overfishing, fishery participants, population or stock, restricted access, sustainable, sustainable use, and sustainability.

Overall Policy on Marine Living Resources

The MLMA's overriding goal is to ensure the conservation, sustainable use, and restoration of California's marine living resources [7050(b)]. This includes the conservation of healthy and diverse marine ecosystems and marine living resources [7050(b)1]. To achieve this goal, the MLMA calls for allowing and encouraging only those activities and uses that are sustainable [7050(b)2]. Although most of the MLMA is devoted to fisheries management, it also recognizes that non-consumptive values such as aesthetic, educational, and recreational values are equally important [7050(b)3].

Unlike previous law, which focused on individual species, the MLMA recognizes that maintaining the health of marine ecosystems is important in and of itself. The MLMA also holds that maintaining the health of marine ecosystems is key to productive fisheries and non-consumptive uses of marine living resources. Furthermore, as in other areas of the United States and the world, restoration of depleted fisheries and damaged habitats is a continuing need.

The words "sustainable" and "sustainability" have inspired mountains of reports and hours of discussion among fisheries managers around the world. At Section 99.5, the MLMA provides its definition. A sustainable fishery is one in which fish populations are allowed to replace themselves. The MLMA recognizes that populations of marine wildlife may fluctuate from year to year in response to external environmental factors, such as climate and oceanography. A sustainable fishery also ensures that marine wildlife can continue providing the "fullest possible range" of economic, social, and ecological benefits. Unlike traditional definitions of sustainability in fisheries, the MLMA's definition calls for maintaining biological diversity.

In Section 7056, the legislature identified the features it believed would foster fisheries that can reliably provide the range of benefits that Californians seek from marine wildlife—sustainable fisheries. These features include limiting bycatch, rebuilding depressed fisheries, maintaining long-term benefits rather than opting for short-term benefits, making decisions transparent, basing decisions on scientific advice and other relevant information, and adapting to changing circumstances. In so many words, the Legislature said that doing these few things would lead to the kind of fisheries that best serve the public interest.

Overall Policy on Marine Fisheries

Within this overall policy on marine living resources, the MLMA sets the state's policy for marine fisheries [7055; 7056]. Both commercial and recreational fisheries are to be managed to assure the long-term economic, recreational, cultural and social benefits of the fisheries and the marine habitats upon which they depend. With this in mind, the MLMA establishes a marine fishery conservation program in order to:
- Achieve sustainable use of fisheries;
- Ensure conservation;
- Promote habitat protection and restoration;
- Rebuild depressed stocks;

- Prevent overfishing; and
- Develop information for management decisions.

The policy also calls for reasonable sport use and encourages the growth of commercial fisheries [7055(c and d)].

The primary management goal of the fishery management system is sustainability [7056]. Unlike other natural resource laws that call for balancing various objectives without indicating any priority, the MLMA places sustainability above other objectives of the MLMA. For instance, while the MLMA calls for considering the interests of fishing communities, it does not place these interests above the long-term sustainability of marine populations.

The fishery management system is to pursue sustainability by achieving a number of objectives, two of which give more detail about sustainability. First, the long-term health of the resource should not be sacrificed for short-term benefits. Second, depressed fisheries are to be rebuilt to the highest sustainable yields allowed by environmental and habitat conditions.

There are several other important features of the MLMA's provisions on sustainability in fisheries. The MLMA recognizes the close linkage between the health of many fish populations and their habitat. Unlike management of most fishing activities, which fall under the jurisdiction of the Commission and Department, protecting and restoring habitat will require working with many other agencies, whose mission may or may not include the conservation of fisheries.

The MLMA recognizes the importance of commercial and recreational fisheries to Californians and the need for allocating marine living resources fairly. The MLMA calls for maintaining fish populations that are sought by sport fishermen at levels that will provide satisfying sport use [7055(c)]. At the same time, the MLMA encourages the growth of commercial fisheries [7055(d)]. The MLMA requires that the effects of regulations be allocated fairly between commercial and recreational fishermen [7072(c)]. It is worth repeating, however, that these objectives are secondary to ensuring that fisheries are sustainable.

SCOPE OF THE MARINE LIFE MANAGEMENT ACT

The provisions of the MLMA are limited geographically [7051(a)]. Unless the authority already existed on January 1, 1999, the MLMA's provisions apply only to ocean and bay waters and not upstream from the mouths of rivers. As mentioned above, the state may manage fishing outside of state waters in certain circumstances.

The fishery management system established by the MLMA applies to four groups of fisheries [7051(b) and 7071(a-c)]. The first group includes fisheries for which the Commission held some management authority before January 1, 1999. Future new regulations affecting these fisheries will need to conform to the MLMA. For example, the constituent involvement standards of the MLMA would apply if new regulations are developed for the commercial sea urchin fishery, or if a fishery management plan is developed, as was the case for the recreational and commercial lobster fishery.

The second group of fisheries includes the nearshore finfish fishery and the white seabass fishery [7071(c)]. The MLMA called for the development and adoption of a fishery management plan for each of these fisheries by January 2002. The Commission adopted the White Seabass FMP in June 2002 and the Nearshore FMP in October 2002.

The third group of fisheries comprises new and growing fisheries that are being managed under the emerging fisheries provisions of the MLMA [7071(c) and 7090]. The Commission may declare a fishery emerging if it meets two sets of criteria. The MLMA stipulated that the first set of criteria be established by the Commission. In October 2000, the Commission approved the following criteria:

- The fishery is not a previously established fishery as determined by criteria set forth in Section 7090(b)(2), Fish and Game Code.
- The Director shall have determined that the fishery has recently exhibited trends which will result in an increase in landings, an increase in the number of participants, or which may jeopardize a stable fishery. In making this determination, the Director shall consider, but not be limited to, an actual increase in landings of the species in question; an increase in the number of applications for experimental gear permits received by the Commission for this fishery; an increase in the amount or efficiency of the gear used in the fishery; or any evidence that the existing regulations are not sufficient to insure a stable, sustainable fishery.

The second set of criteria are set out in the MLMA itself. Section 7090(b)(2) says that an emerging fishery is one that was not established before January 1, 1999. An established fishery is one that had one or more of the following features:

- restricted access,
- a federal fishery management plan regulating catches,
- a population estimate and an annual catch quota,
- regulations considered at least biennially by the Commission, or
- at least two management measures established for sustaining the fishery that appear in the Fish and Game Code or in regulations.

Since adoption of the criteria, the Commission has declared two fisheries emerging: Kellet's whelk and Tanner crab. The MLMA prescribes certain steps once a fishery is declared to be emerging. These steps are described later.

The final group of fisheries are those fisheries for which neither state nor federal fisheries management agencies have adopted regulations. Examples include commercial catches of opaleye, halfmoon, silversides, and some skates. Such fisheries may become candidates for management under the emerging fisheries provisions of the MLMA, and the Commission has the authority to regulate sport catch of any species.

GENERAL POLICIES FOR ACHIEVING THE MLMA'S GOALS

The MLMA includes four general policies for achieving its goals of conservation, sustainable use, and restoration of California's marine living resources: science, constituent involvement, adaptive management, and socio-economic considerations. The application of each of these general policies is reflected in other provisions of the MLMA.

Science

At the core of the MLMA is the principle of basing decisions on sound science and other useful information. With this in mind, the MLMA includes, as a general objective, promotion of research on marine ecosystems that will enable better management decisions [7050(b)5]. The MLMA also calls for basing decisions on the best available scientific information as well as other information that the Department and Commission possess [7050(b)6]. Importantly, the MLMA recognizes the value and importance of relying upon other sources of information such as local knowledge in making decisions regarding the conservation and sustainable use of California's marine living resources [7056(h)]. Additionally, as noted in Chapter 2, the Commission and Department value the traditional ecological knowledge of the tribes and work to incorporate it in the decision-making process.

Within this general policy on science and marine living resources, the MLMA establishes more specific policies for the management of marine fisheries. Generally, fishery management decisions are to be based on the best available scientific and other relevant information, including what the MLMA calls essential fishery information. Essential fishery information includes the biology of fish, population status and trends, fishing effort, catch levels, and impacts of fishing [93]. The MLMA calls upon the Department to collect essential fishery information for all marine fisheries managed by the State in cooperation with participants in the fishery [7060(a and b)].

This kind of information is to form the basis for fishery management plans developed under the MLMA [7072(b)]. Obtaining information shall not substantially delay the development of a plan, however. This provision is intended to ensure that the pursuit of additional information does not delay the adoption of needed management measures, thereby increasing the risk of unsustainable fishing. To foster improvements in the management of individual fisheries, the MLMA requires that fishery management plans include a research protocol that identifies critical information gaps and the steps that will be taken to close those gaps [7081].

To foster the soundness of scientific information used in decisions on fisheries, the MLMA calls for the Department to have the scientific basis for management documents reviewed by external experts [7062(a)], as described below.

Stakeholder Involvement in Management

The MLMA goes beyond traditional public participation in government decision making when it describes the management process. At 7059, the Act characterizes marine life and fishery management as a collaborative process, requiring the involvement of stakeholders and defines stakeholders as "individuals from the sport and commercial fishing industries, aquaculture industries, coastal and ocean tourism and recreation industries, marine conservation organizations, local governments, marine scientists, and the public." At 7059(b), the Act requires that the Commission and Department carry out four activities:

- Review operations in order to improve communication, collaboration, and dispute resolution.
- Develop stakeholder involvement, fact-finding, and dispute resolution processes, as appropriate to each element of the management process.
- Consider the appropriateness of different forms of co-management.
- Pay particular attention to gear used, commercial or sport sectors, and geography of a fishery in involving fishery participants.

The MLMA focuses special attention on the three activities regarding stakeholder involvement in marine fisheries management, requiring that the overall fishery management system meet several objectives [7056(h,k,l)]:

- The process is open and seeks relevant information from interested people.
- Collaborative management is encouraged, and dispute resolution mechanisms are in place.
- The management system seeks to respond to the concerns of participants in the fishery and to changing conditions in the environment and markets, for instance.

The MLMA specifically mentions application of these stakeholder involvement policies in the following fisheries management activities:

- proposing methods to prevent or reduce excess effort in fisheries [7056(e)]
- preparing the annual state of the fisheries report [7065(a)]
- preparing fishery management plans [7076(a)]
- developing the Master Plan for fisheries management [7073(a)]
- developing a process for involving constituents in the preparation of fishery management plans, plan amendments, and research plans in the Master Plan [7073(b)4]
- designing research protocols for individual fishery management plans [7074(b)]
- developing criteria for determining when a fishery management plan may be exempted from peer review [7075(c)]

- proposing plan provisions or plan amendments to the Department or the Commission [7075(d)]
- advising on alternative ways to fund the evaluation of emerging fisheries [7090(f)]

Over the years, a number of stakeholder committees have been formed, such as on sea urchins, spiny lobster, and abalone, for the purposes of informing management or developing FMPs. The legislature has established several other committees, as for abalone, Dungeness crab, squid, herring, and salmon. Usually, membership on these committees is allocated to specific interest groups, such as sport and commercial fishermen, processors, and environmental organizations. Through the MLMA, the legislature also established the Marine Resources Committee of the Commission, which also provides a forum for stakeholder participation.

Less formally, Department and Commission staff speak and correspond with interested individuals, and distribute information through newsletters, on-line blogs, postings to the Department website, press releases, ad-hoc workgroups, and at meetings and conferences. Finally, the Master Plan adopted in 2001 includes a framework for guiding stakeholder engagement in implementing the MLMA. Depending on the situation, the particular issue, and the stage in the decision-making process, meaningful involvement may require conversations in person or by telephone, a newsletter, email, small-group discussions, workshops, large meetings, or hearings.

Other law guides the promulgation of management regulations. The California Administrative Procedure Act (APA) requires that all proposed agency regulations be published in the California Regulatory Notice Register and remain open for public review and comment for a specified period. Among other things, the APA requires that if a hearing is held, notice must be provided 45 days in advance and public comment by mail or at the hearing must be allowed. If the proposed regulation is then changed, the agency must make the revised regulation public 15 days before final action.

The California Environmental Quality Act (CEQA) requires that many projects conducted or permitted by state agencies identify and discuss their potential environmental impact. This involves scoping, identification of project alternatives, and the preparation of an appropriate environmental impact analysis. Such reports must remain open for public comment for a certain amount of time, and public comments must be addressed in revisions of the report. Often, the Commission will adopt a final environmental report in the same meeting at which an FMP or set of regulations is adopted.

Finally, Executive Order B-10-11 issued by Governor Jerry Brown and the California Natural Resources Agency's Tribal Consultation Policy of 2012, the Department's Tribal Communication and Consultation Policy, and the Commission's Tribal Consultation Policy guide government-to-government consultations among the Department, the Commission, and California Native American tribes regarding "the development of regulations, rules, policies, programs, projects, plans, and activities that may affect tribal communities."

Collaboration and Co-Management

While the MLMA provides specific guidance regarding the three activities listed in 7059(b) that touch on stakeholder engagement, it does not do so regarding the fourth activity regarding the Department's consideration of different forms of co-management. The MLMA notes only that co-management "involves close cooperation between the Department and fishery participants, when developing and implementing fishery management plans" [7076(a)]. In practice, there are different forms of co-management, which range from governmental discussions with fishermen to delegation of some management responsibilities to fishing communities.

Since passage of the MLMA, implementing this provision has been stymied by limited domestic experience with co-management of fisheries. Extensive experience with co-management abroad, such as in Australia, New Zealand, Thailand, and Ecuador, suggests that co-management occurs on a spectrum of increasing complexity and re-allocation of responsibility for fisheries management tasks, ranging from data collection to fashioning and implementing management measures. Key components of successful co-management have included a strong governance system, such as California enjoys, as well as a high level of organization among fishermen, which may take the form of centuries-old fishery associations in Japan or *cooperativas* in Mexico and Chile. In California, fish and wildlife resources are held in trust for the people of the state by and through the Department. To some extent, this responsibility to the broader public has served to both limit and shape co-management opportunities and approaches with particular groups.

The MLMA explicitly mentions one fisheries management task on the spectrum of co-management when it discusses fisheries research. In 7060(c), the MLMA states that the Department shall encourage the participation of fishermen in fisheries research, including objective collection and analysis of data and collaboration in research design and carrying out research. There are examples of collaboration between the Department and fishermen in the research arena, which suggest potential for exploring additional forms of co-management in the future. For more than a decade, fishermen in several commercial and recreational fisheries have collaborated with the Department and with independent scientists in gathering data on fish populations. More recently, the Department, Commission, commercial fishermen, and the conservation community have collaborated in the development of an FMP for Pacific herring.

Fashioning a framework for exploring different types and scales of co-management may be necessary if this provision of the MLMA is to be effectively implemented.

Adaptive Management

Conservation and sustainable use of marine living resources are hampered by the limits of our understanding regarding the true status of a resource and its relationships to the larger ecosystem. The many external forces, from climate change to economic trends, that affect human activities and the abundance and distribution of marine life also complicate management. Effective management is also confronted by uncertainty about the extent to which management actions affect a resource compared to or together with other drivers.

The MLMA recognizes the limits of current fisheries management practices and the need to adapt to changing circumstances. It does so by embracing the principle of adaptive management. The MLMA defines this principle as a scientific policy that seeks to improve management "by viewing program actions as tools for learning" [90.1]. Management measures must be designed to provide useful information whether they succeed or fail. Monitoring and evaluation of fisheries are needed to detect the effect of the measures.

The MLMA does not provide guidance on implementing adaptive

THE ADAPTIVE MANAGEMENT CYCLE

DPIPWE 2014 after Jones 2005, 2009   http://www.parks.tas.gov.au/index.aspx?base=5756

management, although it does identify some activities that might be consistent with adaptive management. For example, the MLMA explicitly calls for ensuring that managers can respond to changing environmental and socio-economic conditions [7056(l)]. It also calls for reviewing the overall fishery management system's effectiveness in achieving sustainability and in involving people in a fair and reasonable manner [7056(m)]. Besides requiring the Department and Commission to review their public involvement and communication activities [7059(b)1], the MLMA also requires that the Master Plan for fisheries and fishery management plans include periodic review and amendment [7073(b)5; 7087(a)].

Adaptive management is more than reacting to unexpected events. Instead, the adaptive management cycle begins with explicit description of alternative management strategies, continues with a selection of management actions, their implementation and monitoring, and ends with learning from the performance of the fishery and adjusting management to enhance its effectiveness. The diagram above shows a double-loop version of adaptive management used in Australia that includes both annual adjustments to management as well as periodic, strategic review of the overall management program. In California, this process would be consistent with the periodic review required by the MLMA at 7087(a).

Management strategy evaluation (MSE) is a methodology that fisheries managers have been using increasingly in order to identify and evaluate alternative management strategies and thereby apply adaptive management to fisheries. See Chapter 4 for more information on MSE.

Socio-Economic Considerations

While the overriding goal of the MLMA is to ensure that activities affecting marine life, including fisheries, are sustainable, the Act recognizes other needs as well. Several times in the MLMA, the Legislature referred to the different values and benefits that Californians find in their marine wildlife: environmental, economic, aesthetic, recreational, educational, scientific, nutritional, social, and historic [7050(a)].

Since the MLMA is largely devoted to the management of marine fisheries, it focuses upon the values and interests of fishermen and others interested in fisheries. In general, the MLMA calls not only for maintaining satisfying sport fisheries but for fostering the growth of commercial fisheries [7050(c and d)]. The MLMA recognizes the potential for conflict between commercial and recreational fishing and calls for close coordination in the management of these activities [7056(f)]. The long-term interests of those dependent on fishing for food, livelihood, or recreation receive special mention in the MLMA [7056(i)]. The management system established by the MLMA also shall minimize adverse impacts on small-scale fisheries, coastal communities, and local economies [7056(j)]. Note, however, that these concerns are secondary to the broader mission of fostering sustainable fisheries.

These themes are drawn together in the preparation of fishery management plans. Under the MLMA, FMPs are to summarize information on economic and social factors in the fishery [7080(e)]. If an FMP includes new management measures, it must analyze their anticipated effects on fishermen as well as coastal communities and businesses that rely on the fishery [7083(b)]. Any increases or restrictions on catches are to be allocated fairly among recreational and commercial fishermen [7072(c)].

SPECIFIC TOOLS FOR ACHIEVING THE MLMA'S GOALS

The MLMA identifies several tools for achieving its goals.

- best available information and peer review
- fishery research protocols
- fishery management plans

- fishery management Master Plan
- emerging fisheries
- emergency management
- annual status of fisheries report

Best Available Information and Peer Review

Ensuring the use of the best available scientific information and other relevant information in management of fisheries is an important aim of the MLMA. One step in achieving this aim is external peer review of the information used in management. The discussion below describes the requirements of the MLMA regarding best available scientific information and external peer review.

The MLMA directs that key decisions be based on "the best available scientific information and other relevant information." (The MLMA's formulation differs from the federal Magnuson-Stevens Act in that the latter calls for the use of best available scientific information alone.) These decisions include the following:

- determinations whether a fishery is "depressed" [90.7]
- determinations whether "overfishing" is occurring [98]
- Management of marine living resources [7050(b)6], including fishery management decisions [7056(g)] and fishery management plans [7072(b)]
- dissemination of information on the condition and management of marine resources and fisheries [7050(b)8]
- the effects of management measures on fish populations, habitats, fishermen, and coastal communities [7083(b)]
- identification of measures that might minimize damage to habitat from fishing [7084(a)]
- level of bycatch and its effects on other fisheries, conservation of bycatch species, and the ecosystem [7085]
- identification of criteria for determining when a fishery is overfished [7086(a)]

In Section 7062, the MLMA requires that the Department "establish a program for external peer review of the scientific basis of marine living resources management documents." Peer review, which can range from internal agency review to more intensive review by external scientists in an open workshop setting, is the most accepted and reliable process for assessing the quality of scientific information. Its use as a quality control measure enhances the confidence of the community (including scientists, managers, and stakeholders) in the findings presented in scientific reports and, consequently, in decisions based on that scientific information.

The MLMA identifies some but not all types of documents that must be submitted to external peer review; these documents are "marine resource and fishery research plans" [7062(a)], Interim Fishery Research Protocols [7074(c)], and fishery management plans or plan amendments [7075(a)]. The MLMA does not address data sets, analyses, and other documents developed by the Department or other entities, which may be cited within a management document. Scientific information developed by the Department is subject to the Department's *Policy for Quality in Science and Key Elements of Scientific Work*, which allows internal peer review of documents unless the document will have a substantial management impact or large expenditure of funds.

The MLMA does not provide guidance on other documents that should be submitted to peer review. In general, the Department and Commission could consider for peer review all documents containing scientific information used in the development of fishery management plans and management measures as well as the scientific portions of management documents themselves. The act authorizes the Commission to develop criteria for exempting certain documents from external peer review—specifically, any interim fishery research protocol [7074(d)], fishery management plan or plan amendment [7075(c)].

At a general level, the MLMA characterizes the scope of external peer review as "the scientific basis of marine living resources management documents" [7062(a)]. At 7062(c), the MLMA calls for the external review panel to determine whether "a scientific portion of the document is based on sound scientific knowledge, methods, and practices." Given the breadth of issues in fishery management plans and related documents, properly establishing the scope of an external peer review so that it focuses upon the scientific elements of the documents is crucial to implementing these provisions of the MLMA.

In conducting external peer reviews of scientific information, the act authorizes the Department to enter into an agreement with outside entities "that are significantly involved with research and understanding marine fisheries and are not advocacy organizations" [7062(b)]. In addition to those entities identified in the act, the Department may also contract with any other entity approved by the Commission. The contracted entity is to select and administer the peer review panel and is responsible for the scientific integrity of the peer review process [7062(b)].

Among other things, the act directs that external peer review panels be made up of "individuals with technical expertise specific to the document to be reviewed" [7062(b)]. In addition, "[P]eer reviewers shall not be employees or officers of the Department or the commission and shall not have participated in the development of the document to be reviewed."

At 7062(c), the MLMA requires that the external scientific peer review entity provide the Department with "the written report of the peer review panel that contains an evaluation of the scientific basis of the document," including any findings of scientific deficiencies in the document and the basis for those findings. As required by the MLMA, the Department is to then accept the findings and alter the document, or if it disagrees with a finding, to include as part of the record its basis for its disagreement, including its reasons for determining the document is not based on sound scientific knowledge, methods, or practice.

The act requires that the Department submit the peer review report and its response to peer review findings with the reviewed document to the Commission and to make these materials publicly accessible on the Department's website to strengthen the transparency of the peer review process.

The act is silent regarding the timing of peer review within the regulatory process, and practice has varied. In general, the Department could seek peer review of scientific information that will be used to inform management decisions before regulatory options are developed and before agency or stakeholder positions have hardened, to the extent that is feasible. External peer review of FMPs and similar documents might begin only upon completion of a draft document and before public review. Where feasible, the Department could include an opportunity for the external peer review panel to review the Department's responses to panel findings as well as public comments.

Fishery Research Protocols

As in other respects, the MLMA is proactive regarding assembling information and analyses necessary for effective management. First, the MLMA requires that fishery management plans and amendments contain a fishery research protocol that includes the following information [7081]:

- past and current monitoring of the fishery
- essential fishery information, such as age structure of a population and spawning season, and other relevant information
- plans for additional monitoring and research needed to acquire essential fishery information, including socioeconomic data

The MLMA also recognizes the value in assembling necessary information before FMPs or other management measures are being prepared, and requires that the Department prepare interim research protocols for at least the top three priority fisheries identified in the Master Plan [7074(a)]. In preparing these interim protocols, the Department is to involve fishermen, conservationists, marine scientists and others [7074(b)]. These protocols also must be submitted to external peer review unless the Department determines there is no need, based on criteria approved by the Commission [7074(c-d)]. However, these provisions of the MLMA have not been utilized to date.

Fishery Management Plans

As elsewhere in the United States and the world, the management of fisheries in California has generally been undertaken in a piecemeal fashion. Borrowing from experience with federal fishery management law, the MLMA initiated a more comprehensive approach to fisheries management. The primary vehicle for this approach is the development of fishery management plans for all of the state's major recreational and commercial fisheries. Initially, the MLMA authorized the development and implementation of two fishery management plans: one for white seabass and the other for the nearshore finfish fishery.

Fishery Management Plan Policies

The MLMA emphasizes the role of fishery management plans (FMP) in achieving its goals in managing California's sport and commercial marine fisheries [7070; 7072(a)]. These plans, or FMPs, are to be based on the best scientific information available, as well as other relevant information [7072(b)]. FMPs are to allocate any increases or decreases in allowable catches fairly between commercial and recreational fishermen [7072(c)].

Fishery Management Plan Process

The MLMA makes the Department responsible for developing fishery management plans and implementing regulations, as well as amendments to any existing plans [7075(a)]. The Department may have a fishery management plan developed under contract [7075(b)]. Whether an FMP is developed by the Department itself or by an independent contractor, the Department is to seek the views and help of fishermen, conservationists, marine scientists, and other people, as well as California Sea Grant, NOAA Fisheries, the PFMC, and the Department's own advisory committees [7076(a)].

As in the cases of other decision documents, the scientific basis of a plan is to be reviewed by an independent panel of experts [7075(a)]. The Department is to provide the peer review panel with any written comments it has received from the public regarding the plan [7076(b)]. If the Department determines external peer review is unnecessary, it must provide the Commission with its reasons, based on criteria, which must be adopted by the Commission [7075(a)].

The Department then submits a completed fishery management plan and implementing regulations to the Commission for its consideration [7075(a)]. The Department must also make the plan and implementing regulations available for public review and comment at least 30 days before the Commission holds a hearing on the plan [7077]. Besides informing people who ask to be notified of the plan's availability, the Department must also post plans and hearing schedules on its Internet website.

After the 30-day period, but within 60 days of the submission of the plan, the Commission is to hold at least two public hearings [7078(a)]. The Commission may take action on the plan at the second public hearing or at any later Commission meeting [7078(b)]. If the Commission rejects a plan, including its regulations, the Commission is to provide the Department with its reasons. The Department then has 90 days to revise and resubmit the plan. The Commission then reviews the plan, as before, and either approves or rejects it.

The Commission must adopt implementing regulations within 60 days after approving an FMP [7078(e)]. While adoption of these regulations must follow the Administrative Procedure Act, it does not trigger additional review under the California Environmental Quality Act. If provisions of an FMP adopted by the Commission would supersede any existing statute, the Commission is to provide the Legislature with a copy of the plan before adoption [7078(d)].

While the MLMA itself specifies two fisheries for which FMPs are to be developed (nearshore finfish and white seabass), fishermen, scientists, conservationists, and other people may propose plans or provisions of plans for other fisheries [7075(d)]. After its review of such proposals, the Commission may recommend that the Department develop an FMP or incorporate provisions in an FMP, as proposed.

The process just described also applies to amendments to FMPs.

Contents of a Fishery Management Plan

FMPs are just that: planning documents. FMPs assemble information, analyses, and management alternatives that allow the Department to provide a coherent package of information and management measures to the Commission. FMPs also provide a focus and basis for discussions among scientists, fishermen, conservationists, processors, and other people about the many issues that affect the sustainability of a fishery. Since we have only a limited understanding of how fish populations, their habitats, and human activities change and affect each other, we must make assumptions in selecting management measures for a particular fishery. An FMP can articulate these assumptions, so that they can be tested through monitoring, and improvements can be made in the management of the fishery. Finally, an FMP describes how fishery management measures reflect the standards of the MLMA, from ensuring sustainability to limiting bycatch.

Under the MLMA, fishery management plans are to include at least the seven following elements:
- description of the fishery
- fishery science and essential fishery information
- basic fishery conservation measures
- habitat provisions
- bycatch and discards
- overfishing and rebuilding
- amendment and other modification of an FMP

The MLMA describes each of these elements.

Description of the Fishery

Marine fisheries are complex phenomena, in which fish, habitats, ocean conditions, fishermen, markets, and broader economic conditions all interact. A first step in managing such a complex thing is to describe its parts and their interactions. With this in mind, the MLMA calls for the Department to summarize readily available information about a fishery [7080]. This summary is to include what is known about the following and other types of information:

- The species of fish and their location, their natural history and population dynamics, and effects of ocean conditions
- The habitat of the fish and threats to the habitat
- The role of the target species in the ecosystem and the fishery's effect on that role
- The fleet, fishing effort, and landings by commercial and recreational fishermen
- Economic and social factors in the fishery
- Past conservation and management measures in the fishery

Note that in preparing this and other sections of an FMP, the Department is to seek out the best available scientific information as well as other relevant information that can be obtained without substantially delaying the FMP [7072(b)]. Indeed, there may be little available information in some areas, such as socio-economic factors in a fishery and the population dynamics of individual species of fish or shellfish. The MLMA requires that research protocols identify these gaps and the steps that will be taken to fill them.

Fishery Science and Essential Fishery Information

Management of marine fisheries is more likely to succeed if it is based on solid information and an understanding of the fish and the fishermen. Often, however, key pieces of information are lacking. Furthermore, fisheries change in response to regulations, fishing, markets, and other factors such as climate. Effective management depends on clearly understanding what is known and not known. Collecting information will help us learn how well our view of the workings of a fishery actually track with reality.

Under the MLMA, the vehicle for initiating this critical task is the fishery research protocol that each FMP is to include [7081]. This protocol is to describe the following:

- past and current monitoring of the fishery
- essential fishery information for that fishery
- the time and resources needed to fill gaps in this information
- the steps the Department is taking to monitor a fishery and to obtain essential fishery information

Among other things, "essential fishery information" includes information about the life history and habitat requirements of a species, status and trends in fish populations, effects of fishing on the age structure of a fish populations and on other marine living resources and users, including fishermen and others who benefit [93].

Basic Fishery Conservation Measures

As mentioned above, the primary goal of the MLMA's fishery management policies is sustainability. Sustainability is to be achieved by:

- preventing overfishing
- rebuilding depressed stocks
- ensuring conservation
- promoting habitat protection and restoration

Management and conservation measures are the principal direct means for achieving these goals. The MLMA identifies several types of measures, by way of illustration [7082]:

- limitations on area, time, amount of catch, species, type or amount of gear
- restricted access
- review and adjustment of catch quotas
- personal, gear, or vessel permits and fees

The Department is to incorporate existing management measures into a fishery management plan if they will contribute to a sustainable fishery [7083(a)]. If the Department proposes additional measures, it must summarize anticipated effects on fish populations and habitats, fishermen, and coastal communities that rely on a fishery [7083(b)].

Habitat Provisions

Healthy habitats are important for maintaining the productivity and diversity of marine ecosystems and viable commercial and recreational fisheries. With this in mind, the MLMA calls for minimizing damage to habitats [7056(b)]. While a lot of effort and funding has been devoted to the protection, conservation, and restoration of coastal habitats damaged by development and other activities on land, the effect of some kinds of fishing gear and practices has been largely ignored. However, research has shown that some fishing methods can dramatically alter seabed habitats.

The MLMA recognizes the importance of protecting fisheries habitat from all types of activities, including fishing. It requires FMPs to include measures that minimize habitat damage caused by a fishery [7084]. Measures are limited to those that are "practicable."

The Legislature exempted kelp harvesting from this requirement, since kelp is both a target of the fishery and a habitat. The other requirements of the MLMA will apply to any fishery management plan that might be developed for kelp.

Bycatch and Discards

To one degree or another, nearly all types of sport and commercial fishing gear and practices capture marine life other than the fish that are being sought. For example, trawls fishing for shrimp capture finfish and other marine life. Traps set for lobster may capture finfish as well. Gillnets may catch marine mammals, birds, and sharks. Because of the behavior of rockfish, commercial and recreational fishermen using hook and line often cannot tell which species of rockfish they will catch. Indeed, the only predictably "clean" fishing gears are the harpoon, the spear gun, sea urchin rake, and the human hand. Since discarded marine life often does not survive, unwanted bycatch can be a serious problem.

While recreational and commercial fishermen may retain some bycatch, they discard fish that are of an undesirable species, size, or quality, or that regulations require that they release [91.1]. In the past, such bycatch and discards were so accepted as a part of fishing that they were not even monitored. But the decline of vulnerable species of marine mammals, sea birds, sea turtles, and some populations of fish gradually changed this view. Government agencies, fishermen, and scientists have been collecting information on bycatch in some fisheries. Fishermen and government scientists have also developed several new types of gear and fishing practices that have dramatically reduced bycatch.

The MLMA aims to reduce the impact of bycatch and discards as a matter of standard management of fishing activities. The MLMA calls for making positive efforts to limit bycatch to "acceptable types and amounts" [7056(d)]. To meet this goal, the MLMA requires that an FMP for a fishery with bycatch include information on the amount and type of bycatch [7085]. An FMP is to determine the following:

- the legality of the bycatch
- the threat posed to the bycatch species
- the impact on fisheries that target the bycatch species
- the impact on ecosystems

If the amount or type of bycatch is unacceptable, the MLMA calls for adopting management measures that minimize the bycatch and the mortality of discards that cannot be avoided.

Note that the MLMA defines and addresses bycatch differently from federal fisheries law, which defines bycatch as "fish which are harvested in a fishery, but which are not sold or kept for personal use, and includes economic discards and regulatory discards. Such term does not include fish released alive under a recreational catch and release fishery management program" [16 U.S.C. 1802]. The MLMA, on the other hand, includes marine life other than fish if it is not the target of the fishery, and whether or not the bycatch is discarded [90.5].

One national standard of the federal Magnuson Act calls for minimizing all bycatch. In contrast, the MLMA allows for acceptable types and levels of bycatch. For instance, under-size lobster and crabs may be incidentally captured and released many times before they reach legal size. The MLMA only calls for the minimization of bycatch when the amount or type is "unacceptable".

Overfishing and Rebuilding
During most of the 20th century, the primary focus of fisheries management was the development of fisheries. As government and private investment poured into fisheries and technology developed, the power of fishing fleets grew so that catches were no longer limited by the number or size of fishing boats, but by the size of fish populations. Together with

other factors, such as habitat loss and changes in ocean conditions, this increased fishing power led to overexploitation of some fish populations. Besides damage to ecosystems, overfishing led to economic and social disruption, including lost jobs, higher consumer prices, lost investments, and the decline of fishing communities.

Two of the goals of the MLMA are to prevent overfishing and to rebuild depressed fish populations [7055(b)]. To understand these goals, it is necessary to understand the use of several terms: depressed fishery, overfishing, and overfished.

> **Depressed Fishery:** The MLMA classifies a fishery as depressed if it meets either of two standards:
> 1. If the fishery has been declining over a period of time appropriate for the fishery [90.7]. For instance, a population of a species that fluctuates widely in response to oceanographic changes, such as squid, probably would not qualify as depressed if it declined over a few years. However, more stable populations of longer lived species might be classified as depressed if their abundance were at very low levels for the same number of years.
> 2. If the abundance of a fish population is below the level needed to produce what is called maximum sustainable yield (MSY).

The concept of depressed fisheries is not found in federal fisheries management law, which focuses only what constitutes "overfished" and "overfishing." The MLMA's depressed fishery classification is meant to foster conservation action for populations that are declining for unknown reasons or for a variety of reasons, such as habitat degradation, fishing, and/or changes in ocean conditions.

> **Overfishing:** The MLMA uses MSY also as one standard for determining whether there is overfishing in a fishery. According to the MLMA, overfishing is a rate or level of taking that the Department determines is not sustainable *or* that jeopardizes the capacity of a fishery to produce MSY in the future [98]. The MLMA does not require that the Department determine what the maximum sustainable yield of the fishery is before concluding that overfishing is occurring.

Overfished: If a fish population is depressed, and the principal means for rebuilding the population is a reduction of take, then the fishery is to be classified as "overfished" [97.5].

As a first step in preventing overfishing, the MLMA requires that an FMP include criteria for determining when a fishery is overfished [7086(a)]. This measure, which is borrowed from a broader suite of precautionary measures found in several international treaties, is a major innovation in California fisheries. If properly set, these criteria will provide a way of identifying unsustainable trends in a fishery before it is too late or only when drastic cut-backs in fishing have become inescapable.

If a fishery is already overfished or overfishing is occurring, an FMP is to include measures to prevent or end overfishing and rebuild the fishery [7086(b)]. In these cases, an FMP is to specify a time period in which over-fishing will be prevented or ended and the fishery will be rebuilt [7086(c)]. The rebuilding period is to be no longer than ten years, unless the biology of the fish or environmental conditions call for a different period of time. For example, it may not be possible to rebuild a depressed population of long-lived rockfish in ten years or less. The rebuilding program's restrictions and benefits must be equitably allocated among different parts of a fishery.

Amending and Modifying FMPs

Fisheries change constantly, and climate change may accelerate these changes. Fish populations may change with increasing or decreasing fishing effort or changes in ocean conditions. Commercial fishing effort may change with new technology or new markets. Broader economic trends and newly developing markets can influence commercial fish prices or the affordability of recreational fishing. Our understanding of fisheries also changes, as better monitoring or research provides new information. The ability to effectively implement fishery measures may change through better enforcement or new fishing gear. As a result, FMPs must be able to change.

With this in mind, the MLMA requires that FMPs establish a procedure for regular review and amendment, when that is appropriate [7087(a)]. Because the review and amendment of an FMP is generally a lengthy process, the MLMA allows greater flexibility in responding to changes in a

Maximum Sustainable Yield

Although the maximum sustainable yield, or MSY, of most California fisheries has not been estimated, MSY is such a common standard in fisheries management that it is worth describing. It is important to note that the MLMA does not require the use of MSY as a guide to management.

The MLMA [96.5] defines MSY the same way as federal law: "the highest average yield over time that does not result in a continuing reduction in stock abundance." The MLMA recognizes that factors other than fishing may affect the abundance of a population, and requires that estimates of MSY take into account fluctuations in abundance and changes in ocean conditions.

An MSY model that was developed in the 1950s assumes that a typical population of fish will produce the largest amount of new fish for a fishery when the population has been reduced well below its unexploited size. While the model is quite elegant, it has been criticized on a number of grounds. For instance, the accuracy of MSY estimates depends upon such measures as rates of growth, mortality, and reproduction that are difficult to determine and that change over time. As a result, scientists commonly produce a range of estimates for MSY, based on different assumptions. The trade-offs associated with different assumptions are complex but some generalizations can be drawn. If the higher estimates are used for setting quotas, the risk of overfishing may be higher but so are the short-term socio-economic and political benefits. If the lower estimates are used, the risk of overfishing and the loss of long-term socio-economic and political benefits may be lower, but fisheries may forgo short-term revenues and fishing opportunity.

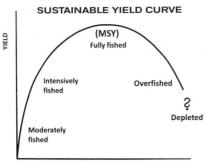

The MLMA defines Optimum Yield or OY as the amount of fish taken in a fishery that does the following: (a) provides the greatest overall benefit to the people of California, particularly with respect to food production and recreational opportunities, and takes into account the protection of marine ecosystems; (b) is the maximum sustainable yield of the fishery, as reduced by relevant economic, social, or ecological factors; (c) in the case of an overfished fishery, provides for rebuilding to a level consistent with producing maximum sustainable yield in the fishery.

fishery by allowing an FMP to specify the kinds of regulations that may be changed without amending the FMP itself [7087(b)]. This process mirrors the federal government's process, where annual quotas or in-season adjustments in management measures may generally be made without resorting to the lengthy process of amending the FMP itself.

The Master Plan for Fisheries

Because the preparation and adoption of FMPs can require considerable time and effort and there are a large number of fisheries, it is critical to set priorities. The Legislature therefore directed the Department to submit to the Commission a Master Plan for the State's fisheries. The Master Plan must identify the resources needed to prepare and adopt FMPs and to list fisheries in order of priority for preparing fishery management plans [7073(a and b)]. In preparing the draft plan, the MLMA requires that the Department seek the help of fishermen, conservationists, marine scientists, and other people. The MLMA requires that the Master Plan include the following elements [7073(b)]:

- A list of the fisheries managed by the state
- A priority list for FMPs, with the highest priority going to those fisheries whose management is least consistent with the policies and requirements of the MLMA
- A description of current research and monitoring of each of the fisheries and any additional efforts needed to obtain essential fishery information for each fishery
- A process that ensures the opportunity for meaningful involvement of fishermen, conservationists, scientists, and others in the development of FMPs and research plans
- A process for periodic review and amendment of the Master Plan

Once the Department has completed its consultations with various interests and has prepared a draft Master Plan, it must submit the draft to the Commission [7073(a)]. The Commission must hold at least one public hearing on the draft plan, then may adopt the plan, or reject it entirely or in part [7073(c)]. The Commission must return any rejected part of the Master Plan to the Department, together with a written statement of the reasons for rejection [7073(c); 7075(a)]. The Department and the Commission then follow the same procedures as for the rejection and resubmission of a fishery management plan [7075(a)]. The Department must revise the rejected parts of the Master Plan and resubmit them to the Commission within 90 days.

Once the Master Plan is adopted, the MLMA requires the preparation of interim research protocols for at least the three highest priority fisheries [7074(a)]. The interim research protocol for a fishery remains effective until an FMP, including a research protocol, is prepared by the Department and adopted by the Commission. Like other such fisheries management documents, the interim research protocol and the FMP must be based partly on the involvement of interested people and peer review [7074(b-d)].

After consultation with stakeholders, the Commission adopted an initial Master Plan in December 2001. In 2016, the Commission and Department initiated an effort and consultations to update the Master Plan.

Emerging Fisheries

A key to sustainable fisheries is to ensure that new fisheries do not make the mistake of growing more quickly than the knowledge and understanding necessary for managing them for sustainability. The Legislature recognized the special place of emerging fisheries in the MLMA by calling for the Commission to "encourage, manage, and regulate" emerging fisheries using the policies of the MLMA [7090(a)].

In the section on Scope of Management above, the criteria were described that the Commission must use in determining whether a fishery is emerging. The MLMA requires that the Department monitor landings and other relevant factors and alert the Commission to new emerging fisheries [7090(c)]. Upon the Department's recommendation, the Commission may then either adopt regulations to limit the catch in the fishery, or direct the Department to prepare an FMP and regulations for the fishery [7090(d)].

In preparing an FMP for an emerging fishery, the Department must follow the MLMA's guidelines [7090(e)]. In addition, the FMP is to include an evaluation period of up to three years—a period that may be extended by the Commission. During this period, the FMP must use such measures as restricted landings or access, as well as time or area closures, to prevent excess fishing effort from entering the fishery [7090(e)1]. These measures must restrict taking in the fishery to levels that the Department determines are necessary for evaluation of the fishery. The FMP must also contain a research plan outlining objectives, methods, and a timetable for evaluating the fishery [7090(e)2].

To support the research and management program, the Commission may impose a fee, which it may reduce in later years [7090(f)]. The Commission and Department must also consult with fishermen and others regarding alternative sources of funding.

As long as they do not conflict with the MLMA, other provisions in the Fish and Game Code may apply to emerging fisheries, particularly to the use of new types of fishing gear, or the use of existing gear in new areas or in new ways [8606(a)]. For example, earlier legislation requires that in order to use new fishing gear or existing gear in new areas or new ways, fishermen must obtain an "experimental fishing permit." The Commission may grant a permit for no more than one year at a time; a permit may be renewed up to three times, until the Legislature approves or disapproves of the use of the gear [8606(a)2]. In granting a permit, the Commission must set conditions to ensure proper use and protection of marine living resources and to minimize conflicts between user groups [8606(a)1]. The Commission is to revoke a permit if it is damaging marine living resources or is creating conflicts among user groups [8606(a)d].

Tanner crab is an example of how emerging fisheries may be explored. Between 2000 and 2006 the Commission issued and renewed three experimental gear permits for catching Tanner crab with a type of trap not previously authorized. The permits imposed a suite of data collection and deployment requirements which were used to inform decision making and the Commission's eventual designation of Tanner crab as an "emerging fishery" per the MLMA. (In more recent years, however, the landings of Tanner crab have been minimal due to the fishery's limited economic viability.)

Emergency Management

The MLMA amended existing provisions regarding emergency management of fisheries. Under the MLMA, the Director of the Department may close or restrict fishing for particular species if the best available scientific or other information indicates the fishing is unsustainable [7710(a)]. Before doing so, however, the Department must hold at least one public hearing in the area of the fishery.

Emergency regulations, which expire within 30 days unless the Commission or Director extends them, may be challenged by appealing to the Commission [7710.1]. The Director may suspend emergency restrictions within 30 days by issuing another emergency regulation under the Administrative Procedure Act [7710.5]. While not directly addressed by the MLMA, it's important to note that the Commission may rely on other authority to close fisheries, and the Department has the authority to close fisheries for public health reasons.

Annual Status of Fisheries Report

Effective fisheries management periodically takes stock of the effectiveness of their programs. Under the MLMA, management is reviewed for its effectiveness in achieving sustainability goals and for fairness and reasonableness in its interaction with people affected by management [7056(m)]. To help ensure that the effectiveness of California's management programs is regularly evaluated, the MLMA requires that the Department prepare an annual report on the status of sport and commercial marine fisheries managed by the state [7065].

While the initial report was intended to include all fisheries managed by the state, subsequent reports are to cover one quarter of the fisheries in a given year [7065(a and c)]. The MLMA directs the Department to involve experts outside the Department, such as Sea Grant staff, other marine scientists, fishermen, and others, in preparing the report.

In assessing each fishery, an annual report must present information on landings, fishing effort and location, as well as other matters that the Department and Commission may decide are relevant [7065(b)]. The contents are currently structured around four topics: the history of the fishery, the status of biological knowledge, the status of the population, and management considerations. Each annual report is to note if a fishery does not meet the sustainability policies of the MLMA [7066(b)]. If a fishery is classified as depressed, the report is to describe the causes, steps being taken to rebuild the fishery, and any recommendations for further action. The report must also describe any habitat problems, including those upstream from coastal bays and waters, and recommend solutions. An annual report must evaluate the effectiveness of the management system in achieving the sustainability goals of the MLMA and the fairness and reasonableness of its dealings with affected people [7066(c)]. The report may recommend changes in the overall management system itself.

Finally, at least every five years, each restricted access program is to be reviewed for consistency with the Commission's Policy on Restricted Access in the annual report. See Appendix D for profiles of existing restricted access programs.

Existing Fishery Management Plans

Since the MLMA was passed in 1998, the Department has prepared and the Commission has adopted four FMPs, one each for white seabass, nearshore finfish, market squid, and spiny lobster. The impetus for preparing each FMP has varied, as has the way in which the FMP was prepared and its final form. Please see Appendix F for an overview of each.

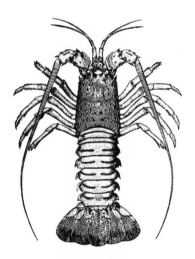

CHAPTER 4

SHAPING FISHERIES
FOR THE FUTURE

AFTER MORE THAN 15 YEARS, the MLMA still serves as a strong foundation for guiding management of the state's ocean fisheries in a systematic, transparent, and science-based fashion. Looking ahead, continued implementation of the MLMA can benefit from the experience of the Commission, Department, and stakeholders in implementing it and from innovations in management and fisheries and ecological science in the United States and abroad. Below are several sources for enhancing implementation of the MLMA and the ecological, economic, and cultural sustainability of the state's ocean fisheries. These include higher level policy documents, such as evaluation of the MLMA's implementation and a strategic vision of the Department, as well as tools and mechanisms that might aid in implementation of specific elements of the MLMA.

LESSONS LEARNED REPORT

In May 2010, a task force sponsored by the OPC and the Commission, in cooperation with the Department, issued its report "Lessons Learned from California's Marine Life Management Act." The report made six basic recommendations:

- Develop an effective management plan for marine living resources, considering the MLMA as one tool among those available.
- Adapt current institutions and policies for greater success within available resources.
- Ensure adequate institutional and policy authority and capacity to achieve the goal of sustainable use of marine living resources.
- Improve management of marine living resources by incremental steps that are feasible given limited resources.

- Systematically increase the scientific knowledge base available to inform management of marine living resources.
- Systematically increase the understanding of available institutions, policies and tools to inform management of marine living resources.

The report also included more specific recommendations regarding setting priorities among regulatory actions, managing species in groups, developing pilot projects in collaborative data gathering, electronic monitoring, setting fees to cover management costs, balancing management actions and data collection, developing a policy on MPAs and fisheries, increasing the Department's credibility as a scientific institution, convening social scientists to define essential socio-economic information and its use in fisheries management.

The report identified impediments to effective implementation of the MLMA. These included a lack of mechanisms for measuring progress and accountability, for setting priorities or for addressing the lack of essential fisheries information, a rigid model for fishery management plans, limited commitment to implementing a collaborative approach to management, limited Department resources for stakeholder engagement, lack of robust data, significant demands on Department staff, and insufficient budget and staff for the Department and the Commission.

The final report as well as supporting materials are available at: http://www.opc.ca.gov/2009/04/mlma-lessons-learned-project/.

CALIFORNIA FISH & WILDLIFE STRATEGIC VISION

Between June 2011 and April 2012, a committee of state and federal agency representatives oversaw the work of a Blue Ribbon Citizen Commission (BRCC) and of a Stakeholder Advisory Group in preparing a strategic vision for the Department and the Commission, as mandated by AB 2376 (Huffman) which was passed and signed in 2010. In April 2012, Resources Secretary John Laird released the final California Fish and Wildlife Strategic Vision. See www.vision.ca.gov.

The final vision included a set of core values, such as stewardship and innovation, as well as foundational strategies, including ecosystem-based management informed by credible science, transparent decision-making, partnerships and collaboration, all of which are consistent with the MLMA. The vision then laid out overarching goals as follows:

- Goal 1: The Department and Commission will build strong relationships with other agencies and governments (federal, state, local and tribal, other organizations and the public).
- Goal 2: The Department and Commission will deliver programs that are valued by the public and services of the highest quality.
- Goal 3: The Department and Commission will achieve outcomes consistent with their missions.
- Goal 4: The Department and Commission will efficiently utilize their resources.

The vision included a set of objectives and actions associated with each goal, such as promoting collaboration and partnerships, developing and applying performance metrics, transparent decision-making based on credible science, seeking statutory changes to create effective deterrents to illegal take, creating greater stakeholder input and exchange.

The vision project also issued two studies. The first assessed the degree to which recommendations from earlier evaluations had been implemented. The second study evaluated whether the barriers encountered in California had been experienced by other organizations similar to the Department and Commission. Overall, the studies found two classes of barriers: external and internal. External barriers, which often are beyond the control of an agency, include conflicting or unclear mandates, procedural requirements, shifts in demographic values and constituent interests, and funding sources and levels. Internal barriers include an organization's culture, hierarchical structure, lack of strong and strategic leadership, reliance on technical rather than policy expertise, lack of a clear vision for staff and stakeholders, and lack of collaborative processes. To overcome these barriers, the final report of the two studies made recommendations regarding funding, setting priorities, organizational change, legislative relationships, stakeholder relationships, communications and public relations, and Fish and Game Commission structure.

Fisheries managers around the world face many of the same challenges. Since passage of the MLMA, a number of new tools and methods have been developed by managers, scientists, fishermen, and others to address these challenges. Below are brief summaries of several of these innovations, as well as summaries of other new approaches to implementing the MLMA.

PRODUCTIVITY AND
SUSCEPTIBILITY ANALYSIS (PSA)

The MLMA recognizes the need to prioritize management across the state's many fisheries. PSA can assist with this objective as a means of scoring a fishery stock's relative vulnerability to overfishing. The current Master Plan includes a prioritization approach that's based on a PSA-like analysis. In a PSA, vulnerability is assessed by providing a score ranging from 1 to 3 for two standardized sets of attributes. The first set of attributes measures the "productivity" of the species, which is mostly derived from life-history characteristics, such as age at maturity and trophic level. The second set characterizes "susceptibility," such as overlap of a stock's distribution with fishing effort, and is designed to assess the species' response to fishing pressure. When data are lacking on a species, information from similar types of fish may be used. Because the PSA gives scores based on ranges of values, the information used can be approximate if precise values are unknown. PSA also includes an index that scores the quality of information and the level of confidence in each attribute. This means that a PSA can be run even in data poor situations, as it is designed to be precautionary in the face of uncertainty. PSA is most informative when a suite of fisheries is scored together.

Together, the productivity and susceptibility metrics are combined to calculate the relative vulnerability of each fishery, which can be displayed graphically on a 2-dimensional chart such as that on the following page. This graphical representation of the vulnerability of a fishery helps ensure that the results facilitate comparisons of vulnerability across fisheries and are easy to understand, making it an ideal tool for stakeholder-based prioritization exercises.

It is important to note that the outputs of a PSA provide no information on the current status of a stock, only the vulnerability to specific fishing behavior. It also does not specify any harvest guidelines or management actions. Instead, the main job of the PSA is to alert managers to those fisheries that are likely to be most sensitive to a particular method of fishing. Another important product is the identification of information that would reduce risk. For example, although a fishery is scored as higher risk if certain information is not available, the score doesn't necessarily mean that the stock is in biological trouble. Filling these information gaps would reduce the risk score. PSA can be an important component of prioritizing

SUSCEPTIBILITY VERSUS PRODUCTIVITY

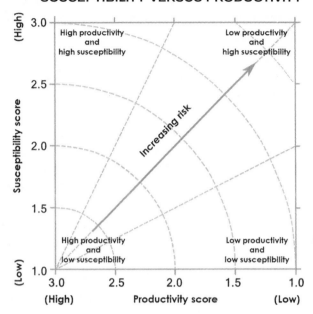

limited management resources across fisheries as well a valuable tool in determining where to focus efforts within a fishery and which types of additional information would be most valuable.

ECOLOGICAL RISK ASSESSMENT

The MLMA emphasizes the importance of maintaining ecosystem health in addition to the health of target species. Ecological Risk Assessment or ERA provides a framework for evaluating the effect of a fishery on the broader ecosystem, including habitat, predator and prey species, etc. As in the PSA, the ecological impact of a fishery depends upon the type of gear used, fishing practices, management measures, and other factors.

There are a number of different ERA frameworks in use around the world. These frameworks have several key features that ensure an ERA is transparent, efficient, cost-effective, consistent, and scientifically credible. Generally, ERA may be applied to both data-rich and data-poor fisheries by incorporating qualitative as well as quantitative information. In this way, an ERA also becomes more inclusive, drawing upon the knowledge and perspectives of stakeholders to identify and assess potential threats to a system. Like PSA, ERA can identify information that may reduce the risk profile of a fishery, thereby making it possible to better target limited financial and scientific resources for gathering high-priority information.

Other capabilities of an ERA might be developed that would allow the Department, Commission, and stakeholders to better understand not only the current threats associated with each fishery, but also which fisheries are most likely to be affected by climate change, ocean acidification, hypoxia, and other environmental changes.

MARINE PROTECTED AREAS

The 2012 completion of a network of marine protected areas (MPAs) under the Marine Life Protection Act creates an opportunity to better understand, integrate, and account for MPAs in achieving the fisheries and ecosystem protection goals of the MLMA. Specifically, MPAs can influence harvest control rules since some percentage of the total biomass of a stock may be protected inside MPAs. MPAs may also influence targets for fishing efforts, provide opportunities for collecting EFI or estimating stock status, and can impact decisions regarding appropriate levels of risk. MPAs can also create unique management opportunities, protect habitat, and can have bearing on the biological and economic considerations that go into fisheries management.

COLLABORATION AND PARTNERSHIPS

The MLMA explicitly encourages the Department and Commission to manage fisheries in collaboration with fishermen and other stakeholders. However, neither the MLMA nor the Master Plan provide guidance that operationalizes this direction. This lack of a framework has frustrated efforts to develop collaborative management arrangements even when partner organizations express an interest in engaging. At the same time, there is widespread misunderstanding about actual opportunities for collaborative management in California fisheries, and the authority for some arrangements under statute and regulation. While the Department is already engaged in some forms of limited collaborative management such as industry consultation and cooperative fisheries research efforts, there are few successful examples of true shared decision making authority. Without such examples to follow, both agency staff and stakeholders have limited knowledge about the potential scope of collaborative management or about the necessary pre-conditions.

At the same time, the Department and Commission do not have the capacity to effectively carry out all important elements of fisheries management, and capacity is unlikely to increase significantly in the coming years. Collaborative management that directs the skills and resources of stakeholders to specific management tasks, such as gathering more detailed information on catches, may offer one source of additional capacity.

Extensive experience with collaborative management, primarily outside California, can be drawn upon to create a framework that the Department, the Commission, and stakeholders can use for identifying, evaluating, and structuring collaborative management activities in a way that increases capacity for effective fisheries management, respects the prerogatives of the Department and the Commission, complies with state law, and inspires stakeholders to assume greater accountability for effective management.

DATA-LIMITED MANAGEMENT

Sustainability is a principal goal of the MLMA. However, management has been constrained by an expectation that it should strive to reduce uncertainty through the application of integrated stock assessments. In integrated stock assessments all available information is simultaneously analyzed with models that find the best fit, including biological reference points related to sustainability. In reality, the widespread lack of data required for these assessment models and their cost limits their use. In the last ten years, techniques for assessing and managing data-limited fisheries, particularly many types of finfish, have advanced dramatically. It is now possible to develop less costly assessments of such fisheries that are of sufficient quality to inform management and guide data collection.

HARVEST CONTROL RULES

The MLMA recognizes the need for adaptive management and to adjust fishing mortality to reflect the changing status of a given population. Most California fisheries operate without such formal rules for reasons similar to those causing the lack of stock assessments. National and international innovations have produced tools for structuring harvest control rules in a more straightforward fashion than was previously done. For example, it has become common practice in federally managed fisheries to set a reference point, such as a level of abundance or spawning potential ratio, below which managers might impose additional restrictions. Similarly, managers might establish a level of abundance that serves as a target for maximizing long-term benefits from a fishery. The California spiny lobster FMP for instance includes such reference points, marking an important step forward in California. Alternative harvest control rules can be assessed using a variety of approaches that openly inform managers and stakeholders of the tradeoffs between varying levels of take and management risk.

MANAGEMENT STRATEGY EVALUATION

Uncertainty is common in fisheries management, from the estimation of biological characteristics of fish species used in stock assessments to the likely performance of specific management measures such as a quota. In recent years, fisheries managers have begun addressing uncertainty by using what is called Management Strategy Evaluation (MSE).

The advantages of the MSE approach are especially relevant for fisheries that are data-poor, where uncertainty is high, and/or that involve multiple, and potentially conflicting, long-term goals. MSE generally involves:

1. An engagement process that provides a forum for fishery managers and participants to engage in collaborative learning, develop shared objectives, and weigh alternative management choices; and

2. A simulation framework (typically a set of linked quantitative models) that reflects best current understanding of the biology of the fished species, how the fishery operates, the effects of alternative management strategies, and interactions among these three elements.

The simulation framework is used to help fishery participants and managers understand and compare the potential effects of different management choices. Importantly, the simulations provide a way to explore tradeoffs, since alternative management strategies may perform differently across the range of objectives identified for a fishery. In addition to informing management choices, the simulation framework also can be used to explore how different kinds of data collection might affect understanding of fish stocks and fishery dynamics, and, therefore, the level of uncertainty in the models. Such analyses can help set priorities for future data collection and potentially allow some estimate of the relative benefits *versus* costs of intensified sampling.

MLMA-BASED ASSESSMENT

The MLMA calls for the prioritization of limited management resources, and an assessment of how identified risks are being addressed by current management is essential. Sustainability scoring frameworks such as those used by the Marine Stewardship Council and the Monterey Bay Aquarium's Seafood Watch Program provide models for analyses that would assess how consistent a given fishery's management is with the MLMA, as required by 7073(b)(2). Such an analysis could include two steps. The first step is an assessment of the degree to which management is consistent with the full range of the MLMA's objectives and requirements. The second is an assessment of the degree to which risks identified in the PSA and ERA evaluations described above are being addressed by current management. The ability to consider consistency with the MLMA, along with how well management is addressing identified risks, will make it possible to focus limited resources on improving the management of those fisheries that pose ecological risks and have clear management gaps, and to do so with an understanding of the types of actions required to bring those fisheries into partial or full consistency with the MLMA.

ECONOMIC AND COMMUNITY CONSIDERATIONS

The MLMA calls for consideration of community impacts of fisheries management measures, and such impacts can be a focus of great stakeholder interest. In fact, the Commission is currently working to understand the community and socioeconomic dynamics at work in California's ports in an effort to make fishing communities resilient in the face of a changing climate. A range of tools are available for evaluating the community impacts of management decisions. Many of these tools have been developed for and used in international development work and can be adapted for use in California. As with economic analysis, community impact analysis should be scaled to the size of the fishery, particularly given the lack of socioeconomic data in general for fisheries, as well as a lack of economists and sociologists within the Department to conduct the analyses.

Describing options for conducting community impact analysis of fishery management measures can help ensure that these impacts are considered in a consistent fashion reflecting best practices and that expectations are realistic. Methodologies developed by NOAA Fisheries Science Centers and by universities in the United States and abroad offer tools for bridging this gap in management.

ENHANCED STATUS REPORTS

The MLMA requires the Department to report periodically on the status of the state's fisheries and identifies four types of information, such as landings and fishing effort, and authorizes the Department and Commission to identify other types. The first Status Reports for California's managed marine living resources were published in 2001 and summarized the available information for each fishery. However, the level of detail differed considerably between fisheries, and the reports generally did not identify what types of essential fishery information were missing. In addition, revising each report every five years, as required by the MLMA, proved infeasible. Finally, the reports are not stored in a way that is readily accessible and have not taken advantage of digital technology so that new information and analysis can be easily incorporated.

Status Reports could be made more relevant to management by broadening the topics covered beyond the four identified in the MLMA itself. A revised format that more fully reflects the MLMA's requirements could facilitate application of a basic standard of MLMA-based management across all fisheries in a consistent and transparent fashion and could serve as a repository of information and analyses, such as those described above. Assembling this information in one place and making it accessible could help the Department in planning both short- and long-term research activities and in identifying needs and opportunities for changes in management. Such enhanced Status Reports could also enable external scientists, including academics and students, to identify research topics relevant to the Department's needs and provide stakeholders with a way to contribute to the characterization of a fishery.

SCALED MANAGEMENT

The MLMA emphasizes the importance of comprehensive and strategic management, primarily through FMPs. However, fisheries vary significantly in terms of the intensity of management effort that may be appropriate. For example, a small, single-sector fishery that presents low ecological risk and is largely consistent with the MLMA may require less management than a large-scale, multisector fishery with conservation concerns and a high degree of controversy. The first type of fishery may require little more than an Enhanced Status Report as described above, and perhaps minor regulatory changes, while the second type of fishery may require a detailed FMP such as those that have been prepared previously.

Identifying a continuum of management responses can be an important means of providing the flexibility needed to bring a greater number of fisheries under MLMA-based management. Additionally, articulating criteria to help identify where on this continuum a fishery should fall would be valuable. On the low end, Enhanced Status Reports may be adequate for simple fisheries with no changes needed. An Enhanced Status Report coupled with a focused rulemaking may suffice for fisheries where only a narrow management adjustment is needed. If more comprehensive management change is required, then some level of FMP may be needed, with the level determined by the fishery's complexity and the degree of management change anticipated. To some extent the Department is already engaging in this type of scaling, but the revised Master Plan could help to both define this continuum and outline the criteria for determining what approach is appropriate for a given fishery profile.

APPENDICES

THE MARINE LIFE
MANAGEMENT ACT

Unless indicated otherwise, all sections were added to the
Fish and Game Code in 1998, and became effective on January 1, 1999.

90

The definitions in this chapter govern the construction of Chapter 7 (commencing with Section 1700) of Division 2 and Division 6 (commencing with Section 5500) and all regulations adopted pursuant to those provisions.

90.1

"Adaptive management," in regard to a marine fishery, means a scientific policy that seeks to improve management of biological resources, particularly in areas of scientific uncertainty, by viewing program actions as tools for learning. Actions shall be designed so that even if they fail, they will provide useful information for future actions. Monitoring and evaluation shall be emphasized so that the interaction of different elements within the system can be better understood.

90.5

"Bycatch" means fish or other marine life that are taken in a fishery but which are not the target of the fishery. "Bycatch" includes discards.

90.7

"Depressed," with regard to a marine fishery, means the condition of a fishery for which the best available scientific information, and other relevant information that the commission or department possesses or receives, indicates a declining population trend has occurred over a period of time appropriate to that fishery. With regard to fisheries for which management is based on maximum sustainable yield, or in which a natural mortality rate is available, "depressed" means the condition of a fishery that exhibits declining fish population abundance levels below those consistent with maximum sustainable yield.

91

"Discards" means fish that are taken in a fishery but are not retained because they are of an undesirable species, size, sex, or quality, or because they are required by law not to be retained.

93

"Essential fishery information," with regard to a marine fishery, means information about fish life history and habitat requirements; the status and trends of fish populations, fishing effort, and catch levels; fishery effects on fish age structure and on other marine living resources and users, and any other information related to the biology of a fish species or to taking in the fishery that is necessary to permit fisheries to be managed according to the requirements of this code.

94

"Fishery" means both of the following:
- (a) One or more populations of marine fish or marine plants that may be treated as a unit for purposes of conservation and management and that are identified on the basis of geographical, scientific, technical, recreational, and economic characteristics.
- (b) Fishing for, harvesting, or catching the populations described in (a).

(Amended January 1, 2003.)

96

"Marine living resources" includes all wild mammals, birds, reptiles, fish, and plants that normally occur in or are associated with salt water, and the marine habitats upon which these animals and plants depend for their continued viability.

96.5

"Maximum sustainable yield" in a marine fishery means the highest average yield over time that does not result in a continuing reduction in stock abundance, taking into account fluctuations in abundance and environmental variability.

97

"Optimum yield," with regard to a marine fishery, means the amount of fish taken in a fishery that does all of the following:

(a) Provides the greatest overall benefit to the people of California, particularly with respect to food production and recreational opportunities, and takes into account the protection of marine ecosystems.

(b) Is the maximum sustainable yield of the fishery, as reduced by relevant economic, social, or ecological factors.

(c) In the case of an overfished fishery, provides for rebuilding to a level consistent with producing maximum sustainable yield in the fishery.

97.5

"Overfished," with regard to a marine fishery, means both of the following:

(a) A depressed fishery.

(b) A reduction of take in the fishery is the principal means for rebuilding the population.

98

"Overfishing" means a rate or level of taking that the best available scientific information, and other relevant information that the commission or department possesses or receives, indicates is not sustainable or that jeopardizes the capacity of a marine fishery to produce the maximum sustainable yield on a continuing basis.

98.2

"Participants" in regard to a fishery means the sportfishing, commercial fishing, and fish receiving and processing sectors of the fishery.

98.5

"Population" or "stock" means a species, subspecies, geographical grouping, or other category of fish capable of management as a unit.

99

"Restricted access," with regard to a marine fishery, means a fishery in which the number of persons who may participate, or the number of vessels that may be used in taking a specified species of fish, or the catch allocated to each fishery participant, is limited by statute or regulation. *(Amended effective January 1, 2000.)*

99.5

"Sustainable," "sustainable use," and "sustainability," with regard to a marine fishery, mean both of the following:

(a) Continuous replacement of resources, taking into account fluctuations in abundance and environmental variability.

(b) Securing the fullest possible range of present and long-term economic, social, and ecological benefits, maintaining biological diversity, and, in the case of fishery management based on maximum sustainable yield, taking in a fishery that does not exceed optimum yield.

CHAPTER 1
GENERAL POLICIES [7050–7051]
7050

(a) The Legislature finds and declares that the Pacific Ocean and its rich marine living resources are of great environmental, economic, aesthetic, recreational, educational, scientific, nutritional, social, and historic importance to the people of California.

(b) It is the policy of the state to ensure the conservation, sustainable use, and, where feasible, restoration of California's marine living resources for the benefit of all the citizens of the state. The objective of this policy shall be to accomplish all of the following:

(1) Conserve the health and diversity of marine ecosystems and marine living resources.

(2) Allow and encourage only those activities and uses of marine living resources that are sustainable.

(3) Recognize the importance of the aesthetic, educational, scientific, and recreational uses that do not involve the taking of California's marine living resources.

(4) Recognize the importance to the economy and the culture of California of sustainable sport and commercial fisheries and the development of commercial aquaculture consistent with the marine living resource conservation policies of this part.

(5) Support and promote scientific research on marine ecosystems and their components to develop better information on which to base marine living resource management decisions.

(6) Manage marine living resources on the basis of the best available scientific information and other relevant information that the commission or department possesses or receives.

(7) Involve all interested parties, including, but not limited to, individuals from the sport and commercial fishing industries, aquaculture industries, coastal and ocean tourism and recreation industries, marine conservation organizations, local governments, marine scientists, and the public in marine living resource management decisions.

(8) Promote the dissemination of accurate information concerning the condition of, or management of, marine resources and fisheries by seeking out the best available information and making it available to the public through the marine resources management process.

(9) Coordinate and cooperate with adjacent states, as well as with Mexico and Canada, and encourage regional approaches to management of activities and uses that affect marine living resources. Particular attention shall be paid to coordinated approaches to the management of shared fisheries.

7051

(a) A regulation adopted pursuant to this part shall apply only to ocean waters and bays. Notwithstanding any other provision of this part, nothing contained in this part grants the department or any other agency of the state any regulatory authority not in existence on January 1, 1999, in any river upstream of the mouth of such river, in the Sacramento-San Joaquin Delta or in any other estuary.

(b) The policies in this part shall apply only to fishery management plans and regulations adopted by the commission on or after January 1, 1999. No power is delegated to the commission or the department by this part to regulate fisheries other than the nearshore fishery, the white sea bass fishery, emerging fisheries, and fisheries for which the commission or department had regulatory authority prior to January 1, 1999.

CHAPTER 2
MARINE FISHERIES GENERALLY [7055–7059]

7055

The Legislature finds and declares that it is the policy of the state that:

(a) California's marine sport and commercial fisheries, and the resources upon which they depend, are important to the people of the state and, to the extent practicable, shall be managed in accordance with the policies and other requirements of this part in order to assure the long-term economic, recreational, ecological, cultural, and social benefits of those fisheries and the marine habitats on which they depend.

(b) Programs for the conservation and management of the marine fishery resources of California shall be established and administered to prevent overfishing, to rebuild depressed stocks, to ensure conservation, to facilitate long-term protection and, where feasible, restoration of marine fishery habitats, and to achieve the sustainable use of the state's fishery resources.

(c) Where a species is the object of sportfishing, a sufficient resource shall be maintained to support a reasonable sport use, taking into consideration the necessity of regulating individual sport fishery bag limits to the quantity that is sufficient to provide a satisfying sport.

(d) The growth of commercial fisheries, including distant-water fisheries, shall be encouraged.

7056

In order to achieve the primary fishery management goal of sustainability, every sport and commercial marine fishery under the jurisdiction of the state shall be managed under a system whose objectives include all of the following:

(a) The fishery is conducted sustainably so that long-term health of the resource is not sacrificed in favor of short-term benefits. In the case of a fishery managed on the basis of maximum sustainable yield, management shall have optimum yield as its objective.

(b) The health of marine fishery habitat is maintained and, to the extent feasible, habitat is restored, and where appropriate, habitat is enhanced.

(c) Depressed fisheries are rebuilt to the highest sustainable yields consistent with environmental and habitat conditions.

(d) The fishery limits bycatch to acceptable types and amounts, as determined for each fishery.

(e) The fishery management system allows fishery participants to propose methods to prevent or reduce excess effort in marine fisheries.

(f) Management of a species that is the target of both sport and commercial fisheries or of a fishery that employs different gears is closely coordinated.

(g) Fishery management decisions are adaptive and are based on the best available scientific information and other relevant information that the commission or department possesses or receives, and the commission and department have available to them essential fishery information on which to base their decisions.

(h) The management decisionmaking process is open and seeks the advice and assistance of interested parties so as to consider relevant information, including local knowledge.

(i) The fishery management system observes the long-term interests of people dependent on fishing for food, livelihood, or recreation.

(j) The adverse impacts of fishery management on small-scale fisheries, coastal communities, and local economies are minimized.

(k) Collaborative and cooperative approaches to management, involving fishery participants, marine scientists, and other interested parties are strongly encouraged, and appropriate mechanisms are in place to resolve disputes such as access, allocation, and gear conflicts.

(l) The management system is proactive and responds quickly to changing environmental conditions and market or other socioeconomic factors and to the concerns of fishery participants.

(m) The management system is periodically reviewed for effectiveness in achieving sustainability goals and for fairness and reasonableness in its interaction with people affected by management.

7058

Any fishery management regulation adopted by the commission shall, to the extent practicable, conform to the policies of Sections 7055 and 7056. *(Amended effective January 1, 2003.)*

7059

(a) The Legislature finds and declares all of the following:

(1) Successful marine life and fishery management is a collaborative process that requires a high degree of ongoing communication and participation of all those involved in the management process, particularly the commission, the department, and those who represent the people and resources that will be most affected by fishery management decisions, especially fishery participants and other interested parties.

(2) In order to maximize the marine science expertise applied to the complex issues of marine life and fishery management, the commission and the department are encouraged to continue to, and to find creative new ways to, contract with or otherwise effectively involve Sea Grant staff, marine scientists, economists, collaborative fact-finding process and dispute resolution specialists, and others with the necessary expertise at colleges, universities, private institutions, and other agencies.

(3) The benefits of the collaborative process required by this section apply to most marine life and fishery management activities including, but not limited to, the development and implementation of research plans, marine managed area plans, fishery management plans, and plan amendments, and the preparation of fishery status reports such as those required by Section 7065.

(4) Because California is a large state with a long coast, and because travel is time consuming and costly, the involvement of interested parties shall be facilitated, to the extent practicable, by conducting meetings and discussions in the areas of the coast and in ports where those most affected are concentrated.

(b) In order to fulfill the intent of subdivision (a), the commission and the department shall do all of the following:

(1) Periodically review marine life and fishery management operations with a view to improving communication, collaboration, and dispute resolution, seeking advice from interested parties as part of the review.

(2) Develop a process for the involvement of interested parties and for fact-finding and dispute resolution processes appropriate to each element in the marine life and fishery management process. Models to consider include, but are not limited to, the take reduction teams authorized under the Marine Mammal Protection Act (16 U.S.C. Sec. 1361 et seq.) and the processes that led to improved management in the California herring, sea urchin, prawn, angel shark, and white seabass fisheries.

(3) Consider the appropriateness of various forms of fisheries co-management, which involves close cooperation between the department and fishery participants, when developing and implementing fishery management plans.

(4) When involving fishery participants in the management process, give particular consideration to the gear used, involvement of sport or commercial sectors or both sectors, and the areas of the coast where the fishery is conducted in order to ensure adequate involvement.

(Amended effective January 1, 2000.)

CHAPTER 3
FISHERIES SCIENCE [7060–7062]
7060

(a) The Legislature finds and declares that for the purposes of sustainable fishery management and this part, essential fishery information is necessary for federally and state-managed marine fisheries important to the people of this state to provide sustainable economic and recreational benefits to the people of California. The Legislature further finds and declares that acquiring essential fishery information can best be accomplished through the ongoing cooperation and collaboration of participants in fisheries.

(b) The department, to the extent feasible, shall conduct and support research to obtain essential fishery information for all marine fisheries managed by the state.

(c) The department, to the maximum extent practicable and consistent with Section 7059, shall encourage the participation of fishermen in fisheries research within a framework that ensures the objective collection and analysis of data, the collaboration of fishermen in research design, and the cooperation of fishermen in carrying out research.

(d) The department may apply for grants to conduct research and may enter into contracts or issue competitive grants to public or private research institutions to conduct research.

7062

(a) The department shall establish a program for external peer review of the scientific basis of marine living resources management documents. The department, in its discretion and unless otherwise required by this part, may submit to peer review, documents that include, but are not limited to, fishery management plans and plan amendments, marine resource and fishery research plans.

(b) The department may enter into an agreement with one or more outside entities that are significantly involved with researching and understanding marine fisheries and are not advocacy organizations. These entities may include, but not be limited to, the Sea Grant program of any state, the University of California, the California State University, the Pacific States Marine Fisheries Commission, or any other entity approved by the commission to select and administer peer review panels, as needed. The peer review panels shall be composed of individuals with technical expertise specific to the document to be reviewed. The entity with which the department enters into an agreement for a peer review shall be responsible for the scientific integrity of the peer review process. Each peer reviewer may be compensated as needed to ensure competent peer review. Peer reviewers shall not be employees or officers of the department or the commission and shall not have participated in the development of the document to be reviewed.

(c) The external peer review entity, within the timeframe and budget agreed upon by the department and the external scientific peer review entity, shall provide the department with the written report of the peer review panel that contains an evaluation of the scientific basis of the document. If the report finds that the department has failed to demonstrate that a scientific portion of the document is based on sound scientific knowledge, methods, and practices, the report shall state that finding, and the reasons for the finding. The department may accept the finding, in whole or in part, and may revise the scientific portions of the document accordingly. If the department disagrees with any aspect of the finding of the external scientific peer review, it shall explain, and include as part of the record, its basis for arriving at such a determination in the analysis prepared for the adoption of the final document, including the reasons why it has determined that the scientific portions of the document are not based on sound scientific knowledge, methods, or practice. The department shall submit the external scientific peer review report to the commission with any peer reviewed document that is to be adopted or approved by the commission.

(d) The requirements of this section do not apply to any emergency regulation adopted pursuant to subdivision (b) of Section 11346.1 of the Government Code.

(e) Nothing in this section shall be interpreted, in any way, to limit the authority of the commission or department to adopt a plan or regulation.

CHAPTER 4
COMMISSION AND DEPARTMENT [7065–7066]
7065

(a) The director shall report annually in writing to the commission on the status of sport and commercial marine fisheries managed by the state. The date of the report shall be chosen by the commission with the advice of the department. Each annual report shall cover at least one-fourth of the marine fisheries managed by the state so that every fishery will be reported on at least once every four years. The department shall, consistent with Section 7059, involve expertise from outside the department in compiling information for the report, which may include, but need not be limited to, Sea Grant staff, other marine scientists, fishery participants, and other interested parties.

(b) For each fishery reported on in an annual report, the report shall include information on landings, fishing effort, areas where the fishery occurs, and other factors affecting the fishery as determined by the department and the commission. Each restricted access program shall be reviewed at least every five years for consistency with the policies of the commission on restricted access fisheries.

(c) Notwithstanding subdivision (a), the first annual report shall be presented to the commission on or before September 1, 2001, and shall cover all the marine fisheries managed by the state. To the extent that the requirements of this section and Section 7073 are duplicative, the first annual report may be combined with the plan required pursuant to Section 7073.

(Amended effective January 1, 2000.)

7066

(a) The Legislature finds and declares that a number of human-caused and natural factors can affect the health of marine fishery resources and result in marine fisheries that do not meet the policies and other requirements of this part.

(b) To the extent feasible, the director's report to the commission pursuant to Section 7065 shall identify any marine fishery that does not meet the sustainability policies of this part. In the case of a fishery identified as being depressed, the report shall indicate the causes of the depressed condition of the fishery, describe steps being taken to rebuild the fishery, and, to the extent practicable, recommend additional steps to rebuild the fishery.

(c) The director's report to the commission pursuant to Section 7065, consistent with subdivision (m) of Section 7056, shall evaluate the management system and may recommend modifications of that system to the commission.

(Amended effective January 1, 2000.)

CHAPTER 5
FISHERY MANAGEMENT PLANS–GENERAL POLICIES
[7070–7074]

7070

The Legislature finds and declares that the critical need to conserve, utilize, and manage the state's marine fish resources and to meet the policies and other requirements stated in this part require that the state's fisheries be managed by means of fishery management plans.

7071

(a) Any white seabass fishery management plan adopted by the commission on or before January 1, 1999, shall remain in effect until amended pursuant to this part. Notwithstanding paragraph (2) of subdivision (b) of Section 7073, any white seabass fishery management plan adopted by the commission and in existence on January 1, 1999, shall be amended to comply with this part on or before January 1, 2002.

(b) In the case of any fishery for which the commission has management authority, including white seabass, regulations that the commission adopts to implement a fishery management plan or plan amendment for that fishery may make inoperative, in regard to that fishery, any fishery management statute that applies to that fishery, including, but not limited to, statutes that govern allowable catch, restricted access programs, permit fees, and time, area, and methods of taking.

(c) On and after January 1, 2000, the commission may adopt regulations as it determines necessary, based on the advice and recommendations of the department, and in a process consistent with Section 7059, to regulate all emerging fisheries, consistent with Section 7090, all fisheries for nearshore fish stocks, and all fisheries for white seabass. Regulations adopted by the commission may include, but need not be limited to, establishing time and area closures, requiring submittal of landing and permit information, regulating fishing gear, permit fees, and establishing restricted access fisheries.

(Amended effective January 1, 2003.)

7072

(a) Fishery management plans shall form the primary basis for managing California's sport and commercial marine fisheries.

(b) Fishery management plans shall be based on the best scientific information that is available, on other relevant information that the department possesses, or on the scientific information or other relevant information that can be obtained without substantially delaying the preparation of the plan.

(c) To the extent that conservation and management measures in a fishery management plan either increase or restrict the overall harvest or catch in a fishery, fishery management plans shall allocate those increases or restrictions fairly among recreational and commercial sectors participating in the fishery.

(d) Consistent with Article 17 (commencing with Section 8585), the commission shall adopt a fishery management plan for the nearshore fishery on or before January 1, 2002, if funds are appropriated for that purpose in the annual Budget Act or pursuant to any other law.

(Amended effective January 1, 2003.)

7073

(a) On or before September 1, 2001, the department shall submit to the commission for its approval a Master Plan that specifies the process and the resources needed to prepare, adopt, and implement fishery management plans for sport and commercial marine fisheries managed by the state. Consistent with Section 7059, the Master Plan shall be prepared with the advice, assistance, and involvement of participants in the various fisheries and their representatives, marine conservationists, marine scientists, and other interested persons.

(b) The Master Plan shall include all of the following:

(1) A list identifying the fisheries managed by the state, with individual fisheries assigned to fishery management plans as determined by the department according to conservation and management needs and consistent with subdivision (f) of Section 7056.

(2) A priority list for preparation of fishery management plans. Highest priority shall be given to fisheries that the department determines have the greatest need for changes in conservation and management measures in order to comply with the policies and requirements set forth in this part. Fisheries for which the department determines that current management complies with the policies and requirements of this part shall be given the lowest priority.

(3) A description of the research, monitoring, and data collection activities that the department conducts for marine fisheries

and of any additional activities that might be needed for the department to acquire essential fishery information, with emphasis on the higher priority fisheries identified pursuant to paragraph (2).

(4) A process consistent with Section 7059 that ensures the opportunity for meaningful involvement in the development of fishery management plans and research plans by fishery participants and their representatives, marine scientists, and other interested parties.

(5) A process for periodic review and amendment of the Master Plan.

(c) The commission shall adopt or reject the Master Plan or Master Plan amendment, in whole or in part, after a public hearing. If the commission rejects a part of the Master Plan or Master Plan amendment, the commission shall return that part to the department for revision and resubmission pursuant to the revision and resubmission procedures for fishery management plans as described in subdivision (a) of Section 7075.

(Amended effective January 1, 2000.)

7074

(a) The department shall prepare interim fishery research protocols for at least the three highest priority fisheries identified pursuant to paragraph (2) of subdivision (b) of Section 7073. An interim fishery protocol shall be used by the department until a fishery management plan is implemented for that fishery.

(b) Consistent with Section 7059, each protocol shall be prepared with the advice, assistance, and involvement of participants in the various fisheries and their representatives, marine conservationists, marine scientists, and other interested persons.

(c) Interim protocols shall be submitted to peer review as described in Section 7062 unless the department, pursuant to subdivision (d), determines that peer review of the interim protocol is not justified. For the purpose of peer review, interim protocols may be combined in the following circumstances:

(1) For related fisheries.

(2) For two or more interim protocols that the commission determines will require the same peer review expertise.

(d) The commission, with the advice of the department, shall adopt criteria to be applied in determining whether an interim protocol may be exempted from peer review.

(Amended effective January 1, 2000.)

CHAPTER 6
FISHERY MANAGEMENT PLAN PREPARATION, APPROVAL, AND REGULATIONS [7075–7078]

7075

(a) The department shall prepare fishery management plans and plan amendments, including any proposed regulations necessary to implement plans or plan amendments, to be submitted to the commission for adoption or rejection. Prior to submitting a plan or plan amendment, including any proposed regulations necessary for implementation, to the commission, the department shall submit the plan to peer review pursuant to Section 7062, unless the department determines that peer review of the plan or plan amendment may be exempted pursuant to subdivision (c). If the department makes that determination, it shall submit its reasons for that determination to the commission with the plan. If the commission rejects a plan or plan amendment, including proposed regulations necessary for implementation, the commission shall return the plan or plan amendment to the department for revision and resubmission together with a written statement of reasons for the rejection. The department shall revise and resubmit the plan or plan amendment to the commission within 90 days of the rejection. The revised plan or plan amendment shall be subject to the review and adoption requirements of this chapter.

(b) The department may contract with qualified individuals or organizations to assist in the preparation of fishery management plans or plan amendments.

(c) The commission, with the advice of the department and consistent with Section 7059, shall adopt criteria to be applied in determining whether a plan or plan amendment may be exempted from peer review.

(d) Fishery participants and their representatives, fishery scientists, or other interested parties may propose plan provisions or plan amendments to the department or commission. The commission shall review any proposal submitted to the commission and may recommend to the department that the department develop a fishery management plan or plan amendment to incorporate the proposal.

7076

(a) To the extent practicable, and consistent with Section 7059, the department shall seek advice and assistance in developing a fishery management plan from participants in the affected fishery, marine scientists, and other interested parties. The department shall also seek the advice and assistance of other persons or entities that it deems appropriate, which may include, but is not limited to, Sea Grant, the National Marine Fisheries Service, the Pacific States Marine Fisheries Commission, the Pacific Fishery Management Council, and any advisory committee of the department.

(b) In the case of a fishery management plan or a plan amendment that is submitted to peer review, the department shall provide the peer review panel with any written comments on the plan or plan amendment that the department has received from fishery participants and other interested parties.

7077

A fishery management plan or plan amendment, or proposed regulations necessary for implementation of a plan or plan amendment, developed by the department shall be available to the public for review at least 30 days prior to a hearing on the management plan or plan amendment by the commission. Persons requesting to be notified of the availability of the plan shall be notified in sufficient time to allow them to review and submit comments at or prior to a hearing. Proposed plans and plan amendments and hearing schedules and agendas shall be posted on the department's Internet website.

7078

(a) The commission shall hold at least two public hearings on a fishery management plan or plan amendment prior to the commission's adoption or rejection of the plan.

(b) The plan or plan amendment shall be heard not later than 60 days following receipt of the plan or plan amendment by the commission. The commission may adopt the plan or plan amendment at the second public hearing, at the commission's meeting following the second public hearing, or at any duly noticed subsequent meeting, subject to subdivision (c).

(c) When scheduling the location of a hearing or meeting relating to a fishery management plan or plan amendment, the commission shall consider factors, including, among other factors, the area of the state, if any, where participants in the fishery are concentrated.

(d) Notwithstanding Section 7550.5 of the Government Code, prior to the adoption of a fishery management plan or plan amendment that would make inoperative a statute, the commission shall provide a copy of the plan or plan amendment to the Legislature for review by the Joint Committee on Fisheries and Aquaculture or, if there is no such committee, to the appropriate policy committee in each house of the Legislature.

(e) The commission shall adopt any regulations necessary to implement a fishery plan or plan amendment no more than 60 days following adoption of the plan or plan amendment. All implementing regulations adopted under this subdivision shall be adopted as a regulation pursuant to the rulemaking provisions of the Administrative Procedure Act, Chapter 3.5 (commencing with Section 11340) of Part 1 of Division 3 of Title 2 of the Government Code. The commission's adoption of regulations to implement a fishery management plan or plan amendment shall not trigger an additional review process under the California Environmental Quality Act (Division 13 (commencing with Section 21000) of the Public Resources Code).

(f) Regulations adopted by the commission to implement a plan or plan amendment shall specify any statute or regulation of the commission that is to become inoperative as to the particular fishery. The list shall designate each statute or regulation by individual section number, rather than by reference to articles or chapters.

CHAPTER 7
CONTENTS OF FISHERY MANAGEMENT PLANS
[7080–7088]

7080

Consistent with subdivision (b) of Section 7072, each fishery management plan prepared by the department shall summarize readily available information about the fishery including, but not limited to, all of the following:

(a) The species of fish and their location, number of vessels and participants involved, fishing effort, historical landings in the sport and commercial sectors, and a history of conservation and management measures affecting the fishery.

(b) The natural history and population dynamics of the target species and the effects of changing oceanic conditions on the target species.

(c) The habitat for the fishery and known threats to the habitat.

(d) The ecosystem role of the target species and the relationship of the fishery to the ecosystem role of the target species.

(e) Economic and social factors related to the fishery.

7081

Consistent with subdivision (b) of Section 7072, each fishery management plan or plan amendment prepared by the department shall include a fishery research protocol that does all of the following:

(a) Describe past and ongoing monitoring of the fishery.

(b) Identify essential fishery information for the fishery, including, but not limited to, age and growth, minimum size at maturity, spawning season, age structure of the population, and, if essential fishery information is lacking, identify the additional information needed and the resources and time necessary to acquire the information.

(c) Indicate the steps the department shall take to monitor the fishery and to obtain essential fishery information, including the data collection and research methodologies, on an ongoing basis.

7082

Each fishery management plan or plan amendment prepared by the department shall contain the measures necessary and appropriate for the conservation and management of the fishery according to the policies and other requirements in this part. The measures may include, but are not limited to, all of the following:

(a) Limitations on the fishery based on area, time, amount of catch, species, size, sex, type or amount of gear, or other factors.

(b) Creation or modification of a restricted access fishery that contributes to a more orderly and sustainable fishery.

(c) A procedure to establish and to periodically review and revise a catch quota in any fishery for which there is a catch quota.

(d) Requirement for a personal, gear, or vessel permit and reasonable fees.

7083

(a) Each fishery management plan prepared by the department shall incorporate the existing conservation and management measures provided in this code that are determined by the department to result in a sustainable fishery.

(b) If additional conservation and management measures are included in the plan, the department shall, consistent with subdivision (b) of Section 7072, summarize anticipated effects of those measures on relevant fish populations and habitats, on fishery participants, and on coastal communities and businesses that rely on the fishery.

7084

(a) Consistent with subdivision (b) of Section 7072, each fishery management plan or plan amendment prepared by the department for a fishery that the department has determined has adverse effects on marine fishery habitat shall include measures that, to the extent practicable, minimize adverse effects on habitat caused by fishing.

(b) Subdivision (a) does not apply to activities regulated by Chapter 6 (commencing with Section 6650) of Part 1.

7085

Consistent with subdivision (b) of Section 7072, each fishery management plan or plan amendment prepared by the department, in fisheries in which bycatch occurs, shall include all of the following:

(a) Information on the amount and type of bycatch.

   (b) Analysis of the amount and type of bycatch based on the following criteria:

   (1) Legality of the bycatch under any relevant law.

   (2) Degree of threat to the sustainability of the bycatch species.

   (3) Impacts on fisheries that target the bycatch species.

   (4) Ecosystem impacts.

   (c) In the case of unacceptable amounts or types of bycatch, conservation and management measures that, in the following priority, do the following:

   (1) Minimize bycatch.

   (2) Minimize mortality of discards that cannot be avoided.

7086

   (a) Consistent with subdivision (b) of Section 7072, each fishery management plan or plan amendment prepared by the department shall specify criteria for identifying when the fishery is overfished.

   (b) In the case of a fishery management plan for a fishery that has been determined to be overfished or in which overfishing is occurring, the fishery management plan shall contain measures to prevent, end, or otherwise appropriately address overfishing and to rebuild the fishery.

   (c) Any fishery management plan, plan amendment, or regulation prepared pursuant to subdivision (b), shall do both of the following:

   (1) Specify a time period for preventing or ending or otherwise appropriately addressing overfishing and rebuilding the fishery that shall be as short as possible, and shall not exceed 10 years except in cases where the biology of the population of fish or other environmental conditions dictate otherwise.

   (2) Allocate both overfishing restrictions and recovery benefits fairly and equitably among sectors of the fishery.

7087

   (a) Each fishery management plan prepared by the department shall include a procedure for review and amendment of the plan, as necessary.

(b) Each fishery management plan or plan amendment prepared by the department shall specify the types of regulations that the department may adopt without a plan amendment.

7088

Each fishery management plan and plan amendment shall include a list of any statutes and regulations that shall become inoperative, as to the particular fishery covered by the fishery management plan or plan amendment, upon the commission's adoption of implementing regulations for that fishery management plan or plan amendment.

CHAPTER 8
EMERGING FISHERIES [7090–7090]
7090

(a) The Legislature finds and declares that a proactive approach to management of emerging fisheries will foster a healthy marine environment and will benefit both commercial and sport fisheries and other marine-dependent activities. Therefore, the commission, based upon the advice and recommendations of the department, shall encourage, manage, and regulate emerging fisheries consistent with the policies of this part.

(b) "Emerging fishery," in regard to a marine fishery, means both of the following:

(1) A fishery that the director has determined is an emerging fishery, based on criteria that are approved by the commission and are related to a trend of increased landings or participants in the fishery and the degree of existing regulation of the fishery.

(2) A fishery that is not an established fishery. "Established fishery," in regard to a marine fishery, means, prior to January 1, 1999, one or more of the following:

(A) A restricted access fishery has been established in this code or in regulations adopted by the commission.

(B) A fishery, for which a federal fishery management plan exists, and in which the catch is limited within a designated time period.

(C) A fishery for which a population estimate and catch quota is established annually.

(D) A fishery for which regulations for the fishery are considered at least biennially by the commission.

(E) A fishery for which this code or regulations adopted by the commission prescribes at least two management measures developed for the purpose of sustaining the fishery. Management measures include minimum or maximum size limits, seasons, time, gear, area restriction, and prohibition on sale or possession of fish.

(c) The department shall closely monitor landings and other factors it deems relevant in each emerging fishery and shall notify the commission of the existence of an emerging fishery.

(d) The commission, upon the recommendation of the department, may do either, or both, of the following:

(1) Adopt regulations that limit taking in the fishery by means that may include, but not be limited to, restricting landings, time, area, gear, or access. These regulations may remain in effect until a fishery management plan is adopted.

(2) Direct the department to prepare a fishery management plan for the fishery and regulations necessary to implement the plan.

(e) A fishery management plan for an emerging fishery shall comply with the requirements for preparing and adopting fishery management plans contained in this part. In addition to those requirements, to allow for adequate evaluation of the fishery and the acquisition of essential fishery information, the fishery management plan shall provide an evaluation period, which shall not exceed three years unless extended by the commission. During the evaluation period, the plan shall do both of the following:

(1) In order to prevent excess fishing effort during the evaluation period, limit taking in the fishery by means that may include, but need not be limited to, restricting landings, time, area, gear, or access to a level that the department determines is necessary for evaluation of the fishery.

(2) Contain a research plan that includes objectives for evaluating the fishery, a description of the methods and data collection techniques for evaluating the fishery, and a timetable for completing the evaluation.

(f) The commission is authorized to impose a fee on an emerging fishery in order to pay the costs of implementing this chapter. The fees may include, but need not be limited to, ocean fishing stamps and permit fees. The fees may not be levied in excess of the necessary costs to implement and administer this chapter. The commission may reduce fees annually if it determines that sufficient revenues exist to cover costs incurred by the department in administering this chapter. The commission and the department, with the advice of fishery participants and other interested parties, shall consider alternative ways to fund the evaluation of emerging fisheries.

(g) An emerging fishery is subject to this section unless the department incorporates the fishery into a fishery management plan developed under Sections 7070 to 7088, inclusive.

(h) In the event that this section is found to conflict with Section 8606, 8614, or 8615, this section shall prevail.

(Amended effective January 1, 2003.)

ARTICLE 17
NEARSHORE FISHERIES MANAGEMENT ACT
[8585–8589.7]

8585

This article shall be known and may be cited as the Nearshore Fisheries Management Act.

8585.5

The Legislature finds and declares that important commercial and recreational fisheries exist on numerous stocks of rockfish (genus Sebastes), California sheephead (genus Semicossyphus), kelp greenling (genus Hexagrammos), cabezon (genus Scorpaenichthys), and scorpionfish (genus Scorpaena), in the nearshore state waters extending from the shore to one nautical mile offshore the California coast, that there is increasing pressure being placed on these fish from recreational and commercial fisheries, that many of these fish species found in the nearshore waters are slow growing and long lived, and that, if depleted, many of these species may take decades to rebuild. The Legislature further finds and declares that, although extensive research has been conducted on some of these species by state and federal governments, there are many gaps in the information on these species and their habitats and that there is no program currently adequate for the systematic research, conservation, and management of nearshore fish stocks and the sustainable activity of recreational and commercial nearshore fisheries. The Legislature further finds and declares that recreational fishing in California generates funds pursuant to the Federal Aid in Sport Fish Restoration Act (16 U.S.C. Secs. 777 to 777l, inclusive), with revenues used for, among other things, research, conservation, and management of nearshore fish. The Legislature further finds and declares that a program for research and conservation of nearshore fish species and their habitats is needed, and that a management program for the nearshore fisheries is necessary. The Legislature further finds and declares that the commission should be granted additional authority to regulate the commercial and recreational fisheries to assure the sustainable populations of nearshore fish stocks. Lastly, the Legislature finds and declares that, whenever feasible and practicable, it is the policy of the state to assure sustainable commercial and recreational nearshore fisheries, to protect recreational opportunities, and to assure long-term employment in commercial and recreational fisheries.

(Amended effective January 1, 2000.)

8586

The following definitions govern the construction of this article:

(a) "Nearshore fish stocks" means any of the following: rockfish (genus Sebastes) for which size limits are established under this article, California sheephead (Semicossyphus pulcher), greenlings of the genus Hexagrammos, cabezon (Scorpaenichthys marmoratus), scorpionfish (Scorpaena guttata), and may include other species of finfish found primarily in rocky reef or kelp habitat in nearshore waters.

(b) "Nearshore fisheries" means the commercial or recreational take or landing of any species of nearshore finfish stocks.

(c) "Nearshore waters" means the ocean waters of the state extending from the shore to one nautical mile from land, including one nautical mile around offshore rocks and islands.

(Amended effective January 1, 2000.)

8586.1

Funding to pay the costs of this article shall be made available from the revenues deposited in the Fish and Game Preservation Fund pursuant to Sections 8587, 8589.5, and 8589.7, and other funds appropriated for these purposes.

8587

Any person taking, possessing aboard a boat, or landing any species of nearshore fish stock for commercial purposes shall possess a valid nearshore fishery permit issued to that person that has not been suspended or revoked, except that when using a boat to take nearshore fish stocks at least one person aboard the boat shall have a valid nearshore fishery permit. Nearshore fishing permits are revocable. The fee for a nearshore fishing permit is one hundred and twenty five dollars ($125).
(Amended effective January 1, 2000.)

8587.1

(a) The commission may adopt regulations as it determines necessary, based on the advice and recommendations of the department, to regulate nearshore fish stocks and fisheries. Regulations adopted by the commission pursuant to this section may include, but are not limited to, requiring submittal of landing and permit information, including logbooks; establishing a restricted access program; establishing permit fees; and establishing limitations on the fishery based on time, area, type, and amount of gear, and amount of catch, species, and size of fish.

(b) Regulations adopted by the commission pursuant to this section may make inoperative any fishery management statute relevant to the nearshore fishery. Any regulation adopted by the commission pursuant to this subdivision shall specify the particular statute to be made inoperative.

(c) The circumstances, restrictions, and requirements of Section 219 do not apply to regulations adopted pursuant to this section.

(d) Any regulations adopted pursuant to this section shall be adopted following consultation with fishery participants and other interested persons consistent with Section 7059.

(Amended effective January 1, 2003.)

8589

Funding to prepare the plan pursuant to subdivision (d) of Section 7072 and any planning and scoping meetings shall be derived from moneys deposited in the Fish and Game Preservation Fund pursuant to Section 8587 and other funds appropriated for these purposes.

8589.5

The commission shall temporarily suspend and may permanently revoke the nearshore fishing permit of any person convicted of a violation of this article. In addition to, or in lieu of, a license or permit suspension or revocation, the commission may adopt and apply a schedule of fines for convictions of violations of this article.

8589.7

(a) Fees received by the department pursuant to Section 8587 shall be deposited in the Fish and Game Preservation Fund to be used by the department to prepare, develop, and implement the nearshore fisheries management plan and for the following purposes:

(1) For research and management of nearshore fish stocks and nearshore habitat. For the purposes of this section, "research" includes, but is not limited to, investigation, experimentation, monitoring, and analysis and "management" means establishing and maintaining a sustainable utilization.

(2) For supplementary funding of allocations for the enforcement of statutes and regulations applicable to nearshore fish stocks, including, but not limited to, the acquisition of special equipment and the production and dissemination of printed materials, such as pamphlets, booklets, and posters aimed at compliance with nearshore fishing regulations.

(3) For the direction of volunteer groups assisting with nearshore fish stocks and nearshore habitat management, for presentations of related matters at scientific conferences and educational institutions, and for publication of related material.

(b) The department shall maintain internal accounts that ensure that the fees received pursuant to Section 8587 are disbursed for the purposes stated in subdivision (a).

(c) The commission shall require an annual accounting from the department on the deposits into, and expenditures from, the Fish and Game Preservation Fund, as related to the revenues generated pursuant to Section 8587. Notwithstanding Section 7550.5 of the Government Code, a copy of the accounting shall be provided to the Legislature for review by the Joint Committee on Fisheries and Aquaculture, and if that committee is not in existence at the time, by the appropriate policy committee in each house of the Legislature.

(d) Unencumbered fees collected pursuant to Section 8587 during any previous calendar year shall remain in the fund and expended for the purposes of subdivision (a). All interest and other earnings on the fees received pursuant to Section 8587 shall be deposited in the fund and shall be used for the purposes of subdivision (a).

— APPENDIX B —

MANAGEMENT ROLES IN SELECT WEST COAST FISHERIES

FISHERY	SECTOR	FISHERY MGT. PLAN	INTERNATIONAL MGT. ORG.	NAT'L OCEANIC & ATMOS. ADMIN.	PACIFIC FISHERY MGT. COUNCIL	CALIFORNIA LEGISLATURE	FISH AND GAME COMMISSION	DEPARTMENT OF FISH AND WILDLIFE
Abalone	Rec	Abalone Recovery and Management Plan. State FMP in development				Penalties for violations	Area and season closures, bag and annual limit, size limit, gear restrictions, conforming actions	Issuing and tracking report cards, status reports, enforcement, monitoring
Anchovy, Northern	Comml	Federal Coastal Pelagic Species FMP		Research and stock assessments, enforcement, FMP approval	Total allowable catch (TAC), FMP preparation, permits	Area restrictions, gear limitations	Permits for reduction fishery	Data collection, enforcement
Bass, Kelp and Sand	Rec	None					Size limit, bag limit, gear restrictions	Data collection, status report, enforcement, monitoring
Bonito	Comml	None				Minimum size and weight limit		Data collection, status report, enforcement, monitoring
Bonito	Rec	None					Minimum size limit, bag limit	Data collection, status report, enforcement, monitoring
Crab, Dungeness	Comml	None		Research		Season and area restrictions, Task Force authorization, permits, trap and size limits		Data collection, trap recovery program, monitoring, enforcement, trap tags and fee collection, season start/end dates
Crab, Dungeness	Rec	None		Research			Season and area restrictions; bag, size, and gear limits	Data collection, monitoring, season start/end dates, licensing fee collection, enforcement
Crab, Rock (all species)	Comml	None				Area restrictions, gear requirements, incidental take	Permits, size limits, gear restrictions, health closures	Data collection, status report, enforcement, monitoring, permit processing
Crab, Rock (all species)	Rec	None					Size, bag limits, health closures, FMP approval	Data collection, FMP preparation, status report development, enforcement, monitoring
Dorado/mahi-mahi	Comml	Federal Highly Migratory Species FMP	Western and Central Pacific Fisheries Commission monitors	FMP approval, stock assessments, WCPFC participation	FMP preparation			Enforcement
Dorado/mahi-mahi	Rec	Federal Highly Migratory Species FMP		FMP approval, stock assessments, WCPFC participation	FMP preparation		Conforming actions	Enforcement

B. Management Roles in Select West Coast Fisheries (cont.)

FISHERY	SECTOR	FISHERY MGT. PLAN	INTERNATIONAL MGT. ORG.	NAT'L OCEANIC & ATMOS. ADMIN.	PACIFIC FISHERY MGT. COUNCIL	CALIFORNIA LEGISLATURE	FISH AND GAME COMMISSION	DEPARTMENT OF FISH AND WILDLIFE
Hake (Pacific Whiting)	Comml	Federal Groundfish FMP	US–Canada Pacific Whiting Treaty	Stock assessment and TAC recommendation with Canada's Department of Fisheries and Oceans; FMP approval	FMP preparation, management of individual transferable quota program			Enforcement
Halibut, California	Comml	None				Area and season restrictions, size limits, permits	Permits, area and gear restrictions for California Halibut Trawl Grounds	Stock assessment, monitoring, status reports, enforcement
Halibut, California	Rec	None					Gear restrictions, bag and size limits	Stock assessment, monitoring, status reports, enforcement
Halibut, Pacific	Rec	None	International Pacific Halibut Commission: management; establish TAC for regions, stock assessment	Implementation of international management measures, division of TAC between states	Recommendations regarding TAC allocations, area closures, division of TAC between Pacific states		Gear restrictions, bag limits, season closures, conforming actions	Data collection, enforcement
Halibut, Pacific	Comml	None	IPHC - Coordinate management, establish TAC for region, stock assessment, set season dates, trip limits,	Implement international management measures, divide TAC between states	Recommendations regarding TAC allocations, area closures, division of TAC among Pacific states; in-season adjustments to bycatch limits			Enforcement
Herring, Pacific	Comml	in development				Permits, gear requirements, area restrictions	TAC approval	Research and monitoring, TAC proposals, permits, annual rule-making, enforcement
Lobster, Spiny	Comml	Spiny Lobster FMP				Permits, season closures, size limits, gear specifications	FMP approval, permits	Data collection, FMP preparation, status reports, trap tags and fees, enforcement, monitoring,
Lobster, Spiny	Rec	Spiny Lobster FMP					FMP approval, report cards, season closures, bag limits, size limit, gear specifications	Data collection, FMP preparation, status reports, enforcement, monitoring
Prawn, Spot	Comml	None					Permit allocation, gear restrictions, area restrictions	Data collection, permit/license processing and fee collection, monitoring, enforcement

B. MANAGEMENT ROLES IN SELECT WEST COAST FISHERIES (CONT.)

FISHERY	SECTOR	FISHERY MGT. PLAN	INTERNATIONAL MGT. ORG.	NAT'L OCEANIC & ATMOS. ADMIN.	PACIFIC FISHERY MGT. COUNCIL	CALIFORNIA LEGISLATURE	FISH AND GAME COMMISSION	DEPARTMENT OF FISH AND WILDLIFE
Federal Groundfish*	Comml	Federal Groundfish FMP		Research and stock assessments, monitoring, FMP approval	Federal FMP preparation, area closures, TACs, manage ITQ, gear restrictions, species specific bag/trip limits, limited entry permits		Species-specific season and area restriction	Biological sampling, population assessments, monitoring, vessel permits/licenses, enforcement
Federal Groundfish*	Rec	Federal Groundfish FMP		Research and stock assessments, FMP approval	FMP preparation, season and area closures, bag and trip limits		Species-specific season and area restrictions and bag limits; prohibited species; conforming actions	Enforcement, monitoring
Nearshore Rockfish**	Comml	Federal Groundfish FMP		Federal FMP approval, stock assessments	Federal FMP preparation, area closures, TACs, manage ITQ, gear restrictions, species specific bag/trip limits, limited entry permits	Area closures, gear restrictions	Implement PFMC regulations; state FMP approval	FMP development, data collection, enforcement, monitoring, status report development, issue vessel permits/licenses
Nearshore Rockfish**	Rec	Federal Groundfish FMP		Federal FMP approval, stock assessments	Federal FMP preparation, season and area closures, bag and trip limits	Area closures	Implement PFMC regulations; state FMP approval	State FMP development, data collection, enforcement, monitoring, status report development
Nearshore Finfish Species***	Comml	Nearshore Fisheries FMP				Area closures, gear restrictions, limited entry permitting	FMP approval, area closures, TACs	FMP development, determine TACs, data collection, enforcement, monitoring, status reports
Nearshore Finfish Species***	Rec	Nearshore Fisheries FMP				Area closures	FMP approval, gear restrictions, seasons, area closures, approval of TACs	State FMP development, TACs, data collection, enforcement, monitoring, status reports
Salmon	Comml	Federal Salmon FMP	Pacific Salmon Commission: management recommendations to US and Canada	Research and stock assessments, in-season management, FMP approval	FMP preparation, TACs, stock assessments, species-specific area, bag, size, gear restrictions, season closures	Permits, species-specific area, size restrictions, season closures		Data collection, enforcement, log book and fee collection
Salmon	Rec	Federal Salmon FMP	Pacific Salmon Commission: management recommendations to US and Canada	Research and stock assessments, in-season management, FMP approval	FMP preparation, species-specific area, bag, size, gear restrictions, season closures	Area closures	Gear restrictions, size limits, species specific bag limits, season restrictions, conforming actions	Data collection, enforcement
Sardine, Pacific	Comml	Federal Coastal Pelagic Species FMP		Research and stock assessments, FMP approval	FMP preparation, TAC, limited entry permits		Permits for collection as bait	Data collection, enforcement

B. Management Roles in Select West Coast Fisheries (cont.)

FISHERY	SECTOR	FISHERY MGT. PLAN	INTERNATIONAL MGT. ORG.	NAT'L OCEANIC & ATMOS. ADMIN.	PACIFIC FISHERY MGT. COUNCIL	CALIFORNIA LEGISLATURE	FISH AND GAME COMMISSION	DEPARTMENT OF FISH AND WILDLIFE
Sea Cucumber	Comml	None				Limited entry permits, bag limits		Data collection, enforcement, monitoring, status reports
Seabass, White	Comml	White Seabass FMP				Gear restrictions and specifications, season closures, size limits	FMP approval	FMP preparation, research, stock assessment, facilitate White Seabass Advisory Committee, hatchery oversight, enforcement
Seabass, White	Rec	White Seabass FMP					FMP approval, bag and size limits	FMP preparation, facilitate White Seabass Advisory Committee, hatchery oversight, enforcement
Shrimp, Pink	Comml	None				Gear requirements	Seasons, area closures, gear requirements, FMP approval	Data collection, enforcement, FMP preparation, monitoring, status report development
Squid, Market	Comml	Market Squid FMP and Federal Coastal and Pelagic Species FMP		Research	Stock monitoring	Restrictions on light use	Catch limit, FMP approval, permits, season closures, gear restrictions	Stock assessment, FMP preparation, data collection, management recommendations, in-season management, permit fee collection and processing, enforcement
Swordfish	Comml	Federal Highly Migratory Species FMP	Western and Central Pacific Fisheries Commission monitors	Research on gear types, manage ESA/MMPA interactions, FMP approval	FMP preparation, new management measures	Gear restrictions, permits	Gear restrictions, permits	Permits, data collection, enforcement
Tuna, all species	Comml	Federal Highly Migratory Species FMP	Inter-American Tropical Tuna Commission: TAC, stock assessment	Implement international management measures, permits and logbooks	Recommends TAC allocations, FMP preparation		Minimum size limit	Data collection, enforcement
Tuna, all species	Rec	Federal Highly Migratory Species FMP	Inter-American Tropical Tuna Commission: TAC, stock assessment	Implement international management measures, issue and process logbooks, FMP approval	Some species-specific bag limits, FMP preparation		Species-specific bag limits, conforming actions	Enforcement
Urchin, Red	Comml	None					Permits, season and area closures, size limits, FMP approval	FMP preparation, status report, permit fee collection and processing, enforcement
Urchin, Red	Rec	None					General invertebrate bag limit, FMP approval	FMP preparation, report card, data collection, enforcement

— APPENDIX C —
STATE FMP
OVERVIEWS

WHITE SEABASS

White seabass (*Atractoscion nobilis*) is the largest croaker species in California waters and is primarily found in the kelp forests off Southern California and Baja California, Mexico. Due to its large size and desirability, it is highly valued by both commercial fishermen and recreational anglers and divers, and has been heavily fished since the 1930s. A dramatic decline of white seabass in southern California and increasing competition between recreational and commercial fishermen during the late 1980s and early 1990s led to a number of management changes. An experimental hatchery program funded by sport fishing stamp revenues was begun in the 1980s to enhance the white seabass population. In 1993, voters adopted a ban on gill net fishing within state waters south of Point Conception, which reduced commercial landings by 70%. In 1995, the legislature directed the Department to prepare a pilot FMP to address population declines.

FMP Development

The White Seabass FMP (WSFMP) was initially drafted before passage of the MLMA; as a result, it has a different structure than later FMPs. After passage of the MLMA, the WSFMP went through two years of public discussion and peer review in order to meet the MLMA requirements. Sections on Essential Fishery Information (EFI) were added, as was content on information gaps and research protocols. The resulting 150-page document is the longest of the existing single-species FMPs, largely because detailed evaluations of the management alternatives required by the California Environmental Quality Act (CEQA) were included. According to the *MLMA Lessons Learned Report*, some participants criticized the FMP for attempting to meet both MLMA and CEQA objectives in one document.

Management Under the FMP

The white seabass FMP identifies the following goals:

1. To manage the white seabass resource for the optimum long-term benefits of present and future generations of Californians.
2. To bring the management of this valuable commercial and recreational species under one authority.
3. To develop a framework for management that will be responsive to environmental and socioeconomic changes.

These goals are accompanied by eight objectives that include sustainable use of the resource, stock recovery, adaptive management, an improved understanding of stock status, and habitat protection. The FMP defines the scope of potential regulatory or management changes that can be made without requiring an FMP amendment. In this way, many management adjustments can be implemented without amending the FMP itself, in response to changes in environmental or fishing conditions or to address resource conservation or socioeconomic issues.

One of the primary objectives of the white seabass FMP is stock recovery. The primary mechanism to achieve this recovery is a quota. Set as part of the FMP process, it is based on the Optimum Yield (OY) as calculated from an estimated pre-exploitation stock size of 40 million pounds. The FMP used an OY of 1.2 million pounds, in order to allow continued recovery of the stock while additional data necessary for a more refined management strategy were collected.

Management of the white seabass fishery is carried out by the Department with the advice of the White Seabass Scientific and Constituent Advisory Panel (WSSCAP), consisting of representatives from the scientific community, recreational and commercial fishers, and environmental groups. The FMP requires the Department and the WSSCAP to evaluate the status of the white seabass fishery against six "Points of Concern" annually, using fishery-dependent data from both Californian and Mexican waters, as well as fishery-independent data on recruitment if available. The points of concern are as follows:

- **Point of Concern 1** examines whether the catch is projected to exceed the current quota. This Point of Concern assumes that there is a stock assessment model available with which to project the coming year's catch. In the absence of such a model, the previous year's catch has been used to determine whether the quota was exceeded, making the management framework reactive rather than proactive. Catch in 2013–14 was well below the quota.

- **Point of Concern 2** assesses whether any adverse or significant change in the biological characteristics of the stock has been discovered, including changes to age composition, size composition, age at maturity, or recruitment. In the 2013–2014 season recreational and commercial fishery length-frequencies showed no significant changes, and no new information on age composition, age at maturity, or age at recruitment was available.

- **Point of Concern 3** assesses the risk of overfishing by evaluating the fishery against three criteria. The first criterion is a 20% decline in the total commercial landings of white seabass for the past two consecutive seasons. This criterion was met in the 2013–2014 season. The second criterion is a 20% decline in both the number of fish and the average weight of fish caught in the recreational fishery for the same two consecutive seasons. While the number of fish landed and the average weight of fish did decline in 2013–2014, the decline did not meet the 20% threshold. The third criterion is a 30% decline in recruitment indices for juvenile white seabass. This criterion was not analyzed in 2013–2014 because funding for monitoring was insufficient in 2009–2011. Sampling was resumed in 2012, but since six consecutive years of sampling are necessary before the recruitment criterion can be reliably evaluated, this criterion is unlikely to be evaluated until 2019–2020. The FMP has been criticized for relying on very limited fishery-independent data. Without such data, only catch-based indicators can be used to detect overfishing. This is a weakness in the management framework, since declines in catch may be driven by other factors, such as a decline in fishing effort.

- **Point of Concern 4** uses the availability of forage species as a factor in the abundance of white seabass. White seabass prey on species such as northern anchovy, jack mackerel, market squid, Pacific mackerel, and Pacific sardine, which are highly mobile and affected by oceanographic conditions. Forage species population levels have been examined using stock assessments of forage fish populations themselves, or, when those have not been not available, commercial fishery landings as a proxy for prey availability. For the 2013–2014 season, forage species were found to be "fairly stable in aggregate."

- **Points of Concern 5 and 6** consider whether any new information on the status of white seabass has come to light, and whether any errors in the data or stock assessment were found. At the time of its development, the management framework specified in the FMP was meant to serve as a placeholder while more data was obtained. In fact, one of the major goals of the FMP was to move the fishery from data-poor to data-rich; to this end, the FMP identifies several short- and long-term goals for collecting more EFI and other monitoring data. To date, however, the fishery remains data-poor, although a stock assessment for white seabass was recently completed and has undergone independent peer review.

NEARSHORE FISHERY

California's nearshore finfish fishery targets a suite of rockfish and other species that inhabit rocky reefs and kelp forests. While there are over a hundred species that inhabit this shallow, coastal environment, a suite of 19 species was chosen for inclusion in the FMP based on their need for management. The assessment of need was based on vulnerability of the species to fishing, demand from commercial and recreational fisheries, co-occurrence in landings, and the species' value to non-extractive users.

While commercial and recreational fishermen statewide had long targeted these stocks, the commercial fishery began to change in the late 1980s and early 1990s in response to demand from the lucrative live-fish market. The increased fishing pressure in shallow waters raised concerns about the potential for local depletion of nearshore finfish populations, whose life history characteristics—long lived, relatively slow growing, with sporadic recruitment success and small home ranges—make them vulnerable to overfishing. In addition, there was concern that growing restrictions in the federally managed deep-water groundfish fishery was driving fishermen into shallow waters. All of these factors made the nearshore fishery a high priority for management actions, even before the MLMA.

FMP Development

The preparation of the nearshore FMP was complicated by a number of factors, including the large number of species found in California's nearshore environment and the overlap between state and federal jurisdiction. Potentially, 124 species found in waters less than 40 fathoms of depth and within state boundaries were eligible for inclusion in the nearshore FMP. Even after excluding all but the most vulnerable species, 19 were included in the plan. Of those species, 16 were already included in the federal Pacific Groundfish Fishery Management Plan, which specifies that any state regulation regarding these species may be more restrictive, but not more liberal than federal rules. Although the Nearshore FMP ultimately called for transferring management of some or all of the shared species to the state, the complexity of the process for amending the federal FMP prevented implementation of this provision of the state Nearshore FMP.

Preparing the nearshore FMP was also made more complex by the large number and diversity of stakeholders interested in the future of the nearshore environment. Hundreds of commercial fishermen held permits to fish for nearshore species, while tens of thousands of recreational anglers and divers from San Diego to Crescent City favored the fishery. In addition, concerns about overfished species sparked the interest of non-extractive users, academics, and environmental NGOs. The resulting group of interested stakeholders had diverse and at times conflicting objectives.

The nearshore FMP was the first plan to be developed entirely under the MLMA and the process exemplified the policies and guidelines of the MLMA. One of the most significant differences between the MLMA and prior fisheries management in California was its emphasis on constituent involvement in decisions regarding marine resources. Stakeholder consultation methods used in developing the nearshore FMP included facilitated meetings with coastal communities, three scoping workshops around the state, and a 37-member advisory panel that met for a series of two-day workshops. The state received and responded to hundreds of comments from the public, which were also incorporated into the development of the plan. By all accounts, it was complicated, complex, comprehensive, contentious, and time-consuming, and consensus building was difficult.

In meeting the MLMA's requirements for the use of best available scientific information and other relevant information, the Department devoted considerable effort to compiling information, and organizing workshops and committees of scientists. The Sea Grant Extension Program (SGEP) was contracted to facilitate the peer review process, in which six independent and anonymous reviewers separately evaluated sections of the FMP and then met to discuss their responses, to identify the significant and recurring issues, and to assist SGEP in developing a procedure to produce the final report. After the final peer review report was submitted, the Commission delayed the adoption of the FMP and instructed the Department to revise the FMP in response to the guidance provided in the peer review report. The anonymity of the reviewers was protected throughout the entire review process.

Many of the reviewers' recommendations were incorporated in the final FMP, including addressing the risk of serial depletion of isolated populations, adoption of more conservative fishery control rules than the PFMC's, and adoption of four state regions rather than three. Other recommendations were not addressed in the final version, such as the inclusion of additional nearshore species, description of fiscal resources needed for acquisition of EFI, and response to the concern that, under the plan, it would be difficult to determine whether a species was actually being overfished. The redrafted section on Fishery Control Rules underwent a second peer review by two independent reviewers.

By some estimates the nearshore FMP cost up to $10 million, although it is not clear how much of this funding was for implementation or for plan development.

Management Under the FMP

The nearshore FMP lays out five goals for the management of the fishery:

1. Ensure long-term resource conservation and sustainability.
2. Employ science-based decision-making.
3. Increase constituent involvement in management.
4. Balance and enhance socio-economic benefits.
5. Identify implementation costs and sources of funding.

The nearshore FMP specifies several objectives for management, including preventing overfishing, rebuilding depressed stocks, ensuring conservation, and promoting habitat protection and restoration. To achieve these objectives, the FMP employs a management strategy that is based on the following five measures: 1) a fishery control rule, 2) regional management, 3) marine protected areas, 4) restricted access, and 5) allocation. Each of these measures is described further below, along with information on how each has been implemented since the adoption of the FMP.

- **Fishery Control Rule**—The nearshore FMP relies on a three-stage control rule that specifies how to set quotas for each of the 19 species based on the amount of information available. In the first stage, a fishery for a species is data-poor and precaution is the primary basis for setting a quota. In the second stage, a fishery is data-moderate—that is, there is enough information to support more traditional forms of single species management, such as stock assessment models. In the third stage, a fishery is data-rich, with enough information to support ecosystem-based management. Before adoption of the nearshore FMP, all nearshore species were considered data-poor. Since implementation, half of the nearshore species have been formally assessed and have moved from the first to the second stage and from setting quotas based on historic catches to setting quotas based on stock assessments.

  The nearshore FMP set thresholds for population biomass at more precautionary levels than the PFMC uses to protect against overfishing and mitigate any ecosystem effects of fishing. For example, under the Nearshore FMP, second stage fisheries are managed using a "60–20" Harvest Control Rule. This means that when a stock's biomass is estimated to be at or above 60% of its unfished biomass, it is considered healthy, but if it falls below this size, allowable catch is reduced in order to rebuild the stock to the healthy level. At 20%, fishing is halted completely.

- **Regional Management**—One of the major components of the nearshore FMP is regional management, which recognizes that rockfish species can vary greatly over relatively small spatial scales and that both commercial and recreational fisheries differ markedly in different regions of the state. Since adoption, the Department has instituted a regional permit system for commercial fishing, and has now established regional monitoring; however, the Department has not had the resources to conduct regional stock assessments and, therefore, cannot set regional quotas.

- **Marine Protected Areas**—Nearshore management under the Nearshore FMP also relies on spatial management via marine protected areas (MPA) to protect habitat and maintain ecosystem integrity. The FMP provides guidance on the siting of MPAs, such as replication of key habitat types and sizing of MPAs to reflect movement patterns and ranges of species. However, the FMP deferred actual designation of MPAs to the Marine Life Protection Act. Additionally, the fishery control rules in the FMP do not include guidance on how to adjust catch levels to account for the biomass within MPAs. It is important to note however, that the statewide network of MPAs eventually established under the MLPA conforms generally with the guidance in the FMP for the function of MPAs in nearshore fishery management.

- **Restricted Access**—The FMP established a restricted access program for 10 nearshore species in 2003. This restricted access program built upon the Nearshore Fishery Permit program, which was established by the Nearshore Fishery Management Act, and structured it around the four regions, each of which had separate permits and so-called capacity goals. In order to transfer a permit from one region to another, two permits must be purchased in the new region, one of which must be retired. Such transfers and non-renewal of permits reduced the total number of permits by 45% between 2003 and 2016. Despite the reduction in the number of permits, each region remains above its capacity goal.

- **Allocation**—Allocation is the division of resource access between different sectors, in this case commercial and recreational fishermen. This issue was one of the most contentious issues in the development of the Nearshore FMP. The MLMA states that FMPs must allocate any increases or restrictions in harvest "fairly" among recreational and commercial fisheries; however, what is "fair" is a hotly debated question. Under the Nearshore FMP, quotas are allocated between commercial and recreational fisheries based on historical regional catches.

Since adoption of the nearshore FMP, the Department has reported on implementation of the plan in two updates, the most recent in 2006. While the report states that full implementation of the plan has been hampered by a lack of adequate funding, lack of Department staff, or a lack of data, the report also highlighted the increased availability of information on the nearshore stocks as well as a collaboration with NOAA Fisheries that resulted in the completion of stock assessments for half the nearshore stocks.

MARKET SQUID

Market squid (*Loligo opalescens*) range from the southern tip of Baja California, Mexico to southeastern Alaska, and play an important role in the food chain as a key forage species for many predatory fish, mammals, and seabirds. Market squid are short lived (6–9 months), dying shortly after spawning. In California, commercial fishermen target market squid using purse and drum seines when squid aggregate in shallow coastal waters to lay eggs. While market squid have been fished in California for more than 130 years, landings dramatically increased in the late 1980s in response to global demand. In terms of volume and revenue, market squid represents one of the most important commercial fisheries in California, generating tens of millions of dollars annually.

The sustainability of the California market squid population is highly dependent on seasonal recruitment, and management of the fishery is designed to balance maximizing commercial take of this valuable resource with ensuring that egg production is sufficient to sustain the population from year to year. Market squid abundance is strongly correlated with environmental factors: squid populations decline in warm water years, but their high fecundity allows populations to rebound quickly in cooler conditions.

Because market squid are also found in federal waters they are part of the Federal FMP for Coastal Pelagic Species (CPS) as a "monitored" species. This means that while no formal stock assessment exists, the PFMC regularly analyzes data on the stock, though the PFMC defers to the state for "active" management of the stock.

FMP Development

The Market Squid FMP was a response to legislative direction rather than the prioritization of fisheries conducted for the Master Plan in 2001. Following a 400% increase in commercial landings of market squid between

1990 and 1997 and an influx of out-of-state vessels, industry sponsored legislation was passed in 1997 placing a moratorium on the number of vessels in the fishery, establishing a $2,500 permit for market squid vessels and light boats, and calling for a three-year study of the fishery to understand the status of the resource.

In response the Department developed and implemented a large-scale monitoring and biological research program. The Department also established a Squid Fishery Advisory Committee (SFAC) and a Squid Research Scientific Committee (SRSC) to advise the Department on research and interim measures. These two committees met from 1998 through 2000 and played a major role in the interim management of the fishery. In 2001, the Department submitted a report on the conservation and management of the fishery.

Shortly after submission of the report, the Legislature passed a bill requiring that management of the market squid fishery be transferred to the Commission by January 2002. As a result, the Department's 2001 report needed to be converted to meet the MLMA requirements for an FMP. In April 2002, the Department issued a draft plan, which underwent extensive peer review. The Department also conducted two public meetings to present options for management of the market squid fishery and received formal public comments on the draft FMP. The Commission adopted a revised FMP in 2005.

During public review, debate focused on two issues: the quota and the proposed permitting system. Regarding the quota, conservation advocates argued that the annual catch limit did not meet MLMA requirements because it was based on a proxy for MSY (i.e., the highest landings ever recorded), not on the more conservative optimum yield, which would likely have been lower to account for uncertainty and ecological impacts. Additionally, these stakeholders suggested that rather than fixed catch limits, the FMP should have based catches on a harvest control rule or other decision-making process, given the natural fluctuations the population experiences. Finally, the quota was criticized for not taking into consideration the needs of species dependence on squid for food, and was therefore neither ecosystem-based nor precautionary.

The other major source of debate was the new permitting system that was intended to reduce capacity. According to the *MLMA Lessons Learned Report*, existing participants and the Department supported proposals to limit effort in the fishery, which was recognized as over-capitalized; however, new entrants wanted access to the fishery. After a lengthy and contentious debate, the Commission changed regulations regarding non-transferable permits, and at its December 2004 meeting, the Commission adopted criteria that effectively negated the stated intent of the FMP to reduce capacity. According to the *MLMA Lessons Learned Report*, later drafts of the Squid FMP eliminated capacity reduction as a stated goal; also, more vessels made commercial landings in 2008 than in 2007. In 2013, the number of seine permits was almost 50% higher than the capacity goal outlined in the FMP.

Management Under the FMP
The goals of the Market Squid FMP are as follows:
1. Manage the market squid resource to ensure long term resource conservation and sustainability.
2. Reduce the potential for overfishing.
3. Institute a framework for management that will be responsive to environmental and socioeconomic changes.

The primary mechanism to achieve these goals is a harvest cap of 118,000 tons per season. The quota was set using multi-year recent average catch for the fishery. This number was supported by a per-recruit population dynamics model called the Egg Escapement Method. The management strategy also includes time and area closures designed to limit uninterrupted fishing effort on spawning aggregations and to ensure that the spawning capacity of the population is maintained. Regarding the third goal of the market squid FMP, there is little in the plan itself that enables timely response to either ecological or socio-economic changes. A table in the FMP indicates that rather than relying on any pre-specified triggers or management responses, achievement of this goal largely rests on the Market Squid Advisory Committee; however, this committee has not been established.

SPINY LOBSTER
California spiny lobster (*Panulirus interruptus*) support a valuable commercial fishery and a significant recreational fishery between Point Conception and the U.S.-Mexico border. The commercial fishery in California landed

approximately 431 metric tons in landings and $18 million in ex-vessel revenue during the 2014–15 fishing season, with the majority of landings coming from the southern portion of the fishery, Los Angeles and San Diego counties. The recreational fishery is estimated to contribute $33–$40 million in consumer spending to the California economy each year.

Spiny lobster biology is well understood. Prior to the FMP, regulations focused on utilizing this information to minimize the impact of fishing on lobster spawning. For example, spawning occurs once a year during late spring through summer; with this in mind, regulations adopted in 1961 closed the fishery during this time, in order to promote successful reproduction. In addition, the minimum size limit, which was adopted in 1955, is designed to allow lobsters to reproduce for one to two years before reaching the legal size limit and thereby becoming available for capture. Spiny lobsters also act as important keystone predators within the southern California nearshore kelp forest ecosystem.

FMP Development

In 2011, a stock assessment concluded that existing restrictions on size, season, gear use, and access to the fishery had resulted in a sustainable level of fishing. However, beginning in 2010, increases in prices paid to commercial fishermen led to a substantial increase in the number of traps pulled per day. This increase in commercial effort spurred concerns about the long-term sustainability of the fishery, the negative consequences to the ecosystem from the deployment of more gear, and the economic health of the commercial fishery. In addition, the recreational fishery, which had traditionally been dominated by divers, shifted towards increased use of boat-based hoop nets, which gave a wider community access to lobster. Increases in fishing effort in both sectors, as well as rising conflict between the sectors, provided an impetus for the development of an FMP, which began in 2012.

In an attempt to reduce cost and departmental workload in preparing an FMP, the Department hired consultants to produce components of the FMP, including segments on natural history, management regulations, monitoring and research, and the economics of the fishery. In addition, a facilitation team was contracted to assist with stakeholder meetings. By contracting out these various segments, the Department was able to retain oversight while reducing its workload. In addition, the FMP benefited from input from a number of scientists from around the world with expertise in lobster fisheries. However, the Department still had to invest considerable effort in fashioning the contractors' products into a concise, coherent product with a consistent format. At 80 pages, this most recent FMP is the shortest of the four.

In order to facilitate communication and build consensus among constituents, the Department formed the Lobster Advisory Committee (LAC). Composed of volunteers representing various stakeholder groups, the LAC was tasked with providing guidance on FMP objectives and end products as well as ideas on management options. Nine LAC meetings occurred between June 2012 and September 2013. One of the more contentious issues brought before the LAC was resource allocation among various users. During the LAC process, constituent representatives were able to formally agree that the current distribution of catch between the commercial and recreational fisheries was acceptable and should be maintained. The LAC also drafted five objectives to guide future allocation considerations for the lobster fishery. Finally, the LAC made a number of recommendations to either clarify or modernize existing regulations. The final form of the FMP was heavily shaped by constituent involvement.

The large number of recreational stakeholders and contention between the southern and northern commercial fleets complicated the public process. One major issue was how to address the escalation of fishing effort in both the commercial and recreational sectors. While there was initial support for a commercial trap limit, the LAC was unable to reach an agreement. To address this stalemate, the Department conducted a survey of commercial fishermen, which found that three-quarters of all respondents were in favor of a trap limit. The results of the survey were presented to the LAC and were used to craft a consensus proposal for a limit of 300 traps per permit and allowing each fisherman to hold a maximum of two permits. The survey reflected opposition to regional trap limits.

The spiny lobster FMP broke new ground by explicitly incorporating California's MPA network into management. In January 2012, 37 new MPAs in Southern California came into effect; together with 13 previously designated MPAs at the Channel Islands, MPAs now cover about 15% of state waters in the region. While it is usually difficult to predict how MPAs will affect nearby fisheries, research in the Channel Islands has shown that the spiny lobster fishery directly benefits from existing MPAs via increased spawning and spillover of larger lobsters from MPA borders. The FMP accounted for the contribution of these MPAs to the spiny lobster stock. A quantitative analysis estimated the proportion of the spawning population protected within MPAs at various fishing levels, and demonstrated that the areas protected from fishing within MPAs provide a buffer against population collapse due to increased spawning output from larger and more abundant lobster within MPAs. In addition, the FMP documents a number of ways that the existing MPAs assist in meeting many of the ecosystem-based goals of the MLMA, including habitat protection and limiting bycatch.

The Commission adopted the final FMP on June 22, 2016; the regulations go into effect in the season beginning October 2017.

Management Under the FMP

The goal of the spiny lobster FMP is to "…formalize a management strategy that can respond effectively to changes in the CA lobster fisheries pursuant to the tenets of the MLMA."

The spiny lobster FMP includes the most comprehensive and adaptive harvest control rule yet developed under the MLMA as a means to detect, prevent, and recover from overfishing by identifying potential conservation problems and prescribing appropriate management responses. It relies on a suite of reference points, a control rule toolbox, and a control rule matrix.

The three lobster reference points are catch, catch per unit effort, and spawning potential ratio. Should threshold reference points be exceeded, eight regulatory options included in the control rule toolbox are available to decision makers to curtail fishing activity. Under conditions of increasing stock health as reflected by favorable reference indicators, provisions are available to expand fishing opportunity. The specific management responses in the toolbox are: change in commercial trap limit, change in recreational bag limit, adoption of a total allowable catch, district closures, change in season length, change in minimum size limit, adoption of a maximum size limit, and establishment of a sex selective fishery (male-only fishery or female-specific size restriction). These options are laid out in an easy-to-read table that describes the challenges and benefits associated with each option.

The third component of the harvest control rule framework is a detailed decision matrix that provides guidance on the appropriate management responses to changes in the fishery. The harvest control rule is discretionary and not every triggering event will necessarily lead to a regulatory response. This process will include consultations with the fishing communities and other stakeholders.

ABALONE

California's coastal waters are home to seven species of abalone, each with different ranges depending on their preference for warmer or cooler waters. Abalone feed primarily on brown algae, often in the form of unattached, drifting kelp. Abalone were collected by aboriginal peoples for food as well as their decorative shells, but sea otter predation kept abalone populations relatively low. However, after the fur trade nearly eliminated otters from California by 1850, abalone populations expanded, fueling the development of a commercial fishery south of San Francisco. Abalone are long lived, slow growing, relatively sedentary, and display episodic recruitment, making them especially vulnerable to overfishing, and abalone fisheries have been closed numerous times since 1913 to allow for recovery. Between 1950 and 1970, the commercial fishery boomed, and over 2,000 metric tons of abalone were landed each year, primarily from southern California. Landings declined after this time, but the high value of abalone kept fishing pressure high.

After years of declines across all species, a bill was passed in 1997 (AB 663) creating a moratorium on all fishing south of San Francisco. This bill also required the creation of the Abalone Recovery and Management Plan (ARMP). White abalone was listed as an endangered species in 2001. A large recreational fishery for red abalone continued in northern California, where surveys indicated that population levels were stable for many years. However, recent declines in this fishery have precipitated the development of a MLMA-based FMP for the long-term management of this fishery.

ARMP Development

AB 663 required the preparation of the ARMP which was to detail the scientific background, interim and long-term goals, alternatives for allocation, costs, criteria for determining when recovery had occurred, and the expected time frame for recovery of abalone populations. The Department assigned a team of biologists to create and refine the ARMP in consultation with many other entities, including the Recreational Abalone Advisory Committee, the Commercial Abalone Advisory Committee, and the ARMP Panel, which included representatives from all constituent groups interested in abalone. The Department also held a commercial constituent workshop attended by commercial fishermen and processors early in the process to gather input on the conceptual plan, and two town-hall meetings to present the draft ARMP to the public and receive informal comments. The draft ARMP also underwent formal, academic peer review in 2002. The draft ARMP was submitted to the Commission for consideration in late 2002.

Due to the high value of abalone, both commercially and culturally, the closure of the abalone fishery was contentious. As a result, the ARMP went through an extensive formal public comment period between 2002 and 2005. Four public meetings were held at locations around the state in 2003 and 2004, and the draft ARMP was revised accordingly. A near-final draft of the ARMP was delivered to the Commission in May 2005. The Commission held five additional public meetings to give the public an opportunity to comment on the final ARMP before its adoption in December 2005.

The ARMP includes nine chapters: an introduction, a biological description of the seven abalone species, the history of the fishery, the legal framework for management, a recovery plan for the closed areas, a management plan for the northern recreational fishery, a description of how the recovery and management plans complement each other, and enforcement and implementation issues. The ARMP was developed during the time that the MLMA was passed and implemented, but it adhered to the requirements outlined in AB 663 rather than to the MLMA.

At the time of ARMP adoption, the Commission also directed the Department to begin considering resumption of a limited commercial fishery for red abalone at San Miguel Island. San Miguel Island is the north-western-most of the Channel Islands, and population levels had remained stable in contrast to the declines seen elsewhere in southern California waters. The Department initiated a participatory process to assess the population at San Miguel Island against the ARMP criteria for recovery, including convening an Abalone Advisory Group and conducting collaborative resource surveys over three years at San Miguel Island. A consultant was hired to assess the data in these surveys; however, the results from the modeling work were of limited use due to constraints in the data. In 2010 the Commission suspended consideration of resuming a fishery at San Miguel Island until a more refined analysis with stock projections over a longer time frame could be completed.

Management Under the ARMP

The ARMP was designed as an interim plan. It specifies a recovery plan for the southern abalone stocks as well as a precautionary management plan for the northern fishery, but its objective is to move the fishery towards a long term regional adaptive management plan.

The ARMP specifies the criteria for defining when abalone stocks are overfished, and when they have recovered. The primary criterion used to evaluate population health is density, defined as the number of animals in a given area. The plan lays out a trigger density (also known as the minimum viable population size) of 2,000 abalone per hectare. Below this density, populations are at risk of recruitment failure, and fishing must be stopped until recovery is achieved. The recovery target density of 6,600 abalone per hectare must be achieved before fishing can be resumed. Abalone populations at densities between the trigger and the target densities are in the precautionary zone, and additional management actions may be required to limit fishing and foster recovery. The size structure of the population is also evaluated to ensure that there are both young and old individuals in the population.

Under the ARMP, the northern recreational fishery which had densities above the target density when the ARMP was passed, was managed using size limits, bag limits, a report card, and seasonal restrictions. Fishery independent surveys were conducted annually at index sites to monitor densities. Between 2009 and 2012, densities in Sonoma County declined by 60% compared to pre-2007 levels. While high levels of fishing contributed to these declines, they were exacerbated by a harmful algal bloom, which resulted in mass mortalities in 2011. In response, an annual limit of 18 abalone, including 9 taken from Sonoma County, was instituted to reduce catches, and fishing was further restricted in terms of time and location, with one popular fishing site being closed.

FMP Development

In 2014, in response to the declines of red abalone at index sites in northern California, the Department asked the Commission to consider either an amendment of the ARMP to address the evolving management needs of the northern California recreational fishery, or to create a separate FMP for the fishery. Following the recommendation of the Marine Resources Committee, the Commission requested that the Department prepare an FMP. There was concern from stakeholders that the decision to prepare an FMP for the northern fishery signaled a lack of focus on recovery and re-opening of southern fisheries. However, given that the northern fishery was showing signs of stress under the current management procedure, it was deemed that there was an urgent need for an FMP. Since that time, warm water conditions have reduced the amount of kelp available for abalone, placing further stress on the population.

In 2014, four public scoping workshops were held around California to give stakeholders an opportunity to contribute ideas about how abalone management could be improved. In addition, the department conducted a survey of abalone fishermen in February 2015 to determine fishermen's priorities and preferences regarding the northern California red abalone recreational fishery and management practices. Comments from these two processes largely focused on concerns about the Department's current survey methodology, and the selection of index sites. In 2016, Department biologists began preparing a draft FMP, which is slated for public comment and peer review in the summer of 2017, and implementation in 2018.

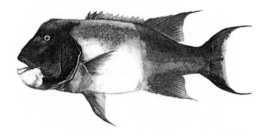

— APPENDIX D —

RESTRICTED ACCESS PROGRAMS IN CALIFORNIA FISHERIES

PERMIT	SPECIES	PRIMARY MANAGEMENT AUTHORITY	IMPLEMENTATION YEAR	PERMIT HOLDER	PRIMARY TRANSFER CONDITIONS	NUMBER OF TIERS (IF ANY)	VESSEL SIZE ENDORSEMENTS (IF ANY)	REGIONAL ENDORSEMENTS (IF ANY)	GEAR	PERMITS 2015
California Halibut Bottom Trawl	California Halibut	Commission	2006	Commercial vessel owner		0	Length		Trawl	42
Coastal Pelagics	Northern anchovy Pacific mackerel Pacific sardine Jack mackerel	Pacific Fishery Management Council	2000	Vessel	Receiving vessel must have gross tonnage equal to or greater than original vessel plus 10%	0	Gross tonnage		Seine	Anchovy: 71
Nearshore finfish	Black & yellow rockfish Gopher rockfish Kelp rockfish Calif. scorpionfish Greenlings of genus *Hexagrammos* China rockfish Grass rockfish Calif. Sheephead Cabezon	Commission (consistent with the Federal Groundfish FMP)	1999	Individual fisherman on board vessel	To holder of California Commercial Fishing License	0		North Coast North-Central Coast South-Central Coast South Coast	Trap Hook/line	Bycatch 12 trap 57 other 145
Deeper nearshore finfish	Black rockfish Blue rockfish Brown rockfish Calico rockfish Copper rockfish Olive rockfish Quillback rockfish Treefish	Commission (consistent with the Federal Groundfish FMP)	1999	Individual fisherman on board vessel		0			Trap Hook/line	185
Drift gill net	Sharks Swordfish	Pacific Fishery Management Council FMP; California issues permits	1984	Individual fisherman on board vessel	Permit held for three or more years OR permittee unable to use permit due to death or hardship AND new permittee has a general drift gillnet permit.	0			Drift gill net	73

134

D. Restricted Access Programs in California Fisheries (cont.)

PERMIT	SPECIES	PRIMARY MANAGEMENT AUTHORITY	IMPLEMENTATION YEAR	PERMIT HOLDER	PRIMARY TRANSFER CONDITIONS	NUMBER OF TIERS (IF ANY)	VESSEL SIZE ENDORSEMENTS (IF ANY)	REGIONAL ENDORSEMENTS (IF ANY)	GEAR	PERMITS 2015
Dungeness crab	Dungeness crab	Legislature	1995	Vessel owner	Vessel owner may transfer license to another vessel they own if that vessel is a similar size.	7			Trap	489
Gill/trammel net	Nearshore species (e.g., white seabass, California halibut, and lingcod)	Legislature and Commission	1985	Individual fisherman on board vessel	Individual receiving permit must have previous experience working gill or trammel nets and pass a proficiency test administered by the Department.	0			Gill/trammel net	125
Herring	Pacific herring	Commission	1986	Vessel owner for permit and stamp for qualifying vessel	Individual receiving the permit has 20 or more herring points	0			Gill/trammel net	131
Lobster	California spiny lobster	Legislature and Commission	1996	Individual fisherman	Original owner of a transferable lobster operator permit that has not been suspended or revoked may transfer his/her permit to another person licensed as a California commercial fisherman	0			Trap	189
Market squid	Market squid	Commission	1998	Vessel	Vessel receiving permit must have comparable gross tonnage to the sum of the gross tonnage of vessels transferring their permits	0	Gross tonnage		Seine, brail, light boat	75 vessels 44 brail 34 light boats
Northern Pink Shrimp	Pink shrimp	Commission	1994	Vessel owner	May be transferred to another vessel owned by the permittee that is no greater than 5 ft longer than the original size endorsement of the permit.	0	Vessel length	North of Point Conception	Trawl	35

D. Restricted Access Programs in California Fisheries (cont.)

PERMIT	SPECIES	PRIMARY MANAGEMENT AUTHORITY	IMPLEMENTATION YEAR	PERMIT HOLDER	PRIMARY TRANSFER CONDITIONS	NUMBER OF TIERS (IF ANY)	VESSEL SIZE ENDORSEMENTS (IF ANY)	REGIONAL ENDORSEMENTS (IF ANY)	GEAR	PERMITS 2015
Salmon	Chinook salmon Coho salmon Pink salmon	Pacific Fishery Management Council	1983	Vessel owner	May be transferred to another vessel owned by the permittee of an equal or lesser fishing capacity	0			Troll	1,130
Sea cucumber trawl	California sea cucumber and warty sea cucumber	Commission	1997	Individual fisherman on board vessel	Original permittee has previously held a valid sea cucumber permit for any four permit years and landed at least 100 pounds and their permit has not been suspended or revoked and individual receiving permit has a California commercial fishing license that has not been suspended or revoked	0			Trawl	16
Sea cucumber dive	California sea cucumber and warty sea cucumber	Legislature and Commission	1989	Individual fisherman	Original permittee has previously held a valid sea cucumber permit for any four permit years and landed at least 100 pounds and their permit has not been suspended or revoked and individual receiving permit has a California commercial fishing license that has not been suspended or revoked	0			Dive	83
Sea urchin	Red sea urchin	Commission	1989	Individual fisherman		0			Dive	304
Southern rock crab	Brown, yellow and red rock crab	Commission	2003	Individual fisherman	Individual receiving permit must have California commercial fishing license	0			Trap	122
Spot prawn	Spot prawn	Commission	2002	Vessel owner	Owner may transfer permit to another vessel they own or to another owner of a vessel that is qualified for the fishery	3			Trap	25

FEDERAL FMP
OVERVIEWS

PACIFIC GROUNDFISH
FISHERY MANAGEMENT PLAN

The PFMC's fishery management plan (FMP) for groundfish includes approximately 90 species of finfish, most of which live on or near the ocean bottom. These species fall into five categories:

- sixty-four species of rockfish, including 15 managed jointly with the State of California through the Nearshore Fishery Management Plan, such as black rockfish, blue rockfish, grass rockfish, and China rockfish. Other notable species are widow rockfish, cowcod, and Pacific ocean perch
- twelve species of flatfish, including petrale sole, starry flounder, and Pacific sanddab
- six species of groundfish, such as lingcod, cabezon, kelp greenling, and sablefish
- six species of sharks and skates including leopard and soupfin sharks, spiny dogfish, and three species of skate
- miscellaneous species, including ratfish and Pacific rattail grenadier

The groundfish FMP manages fishing by different groups or sectors of fishermen, each with its own permits and rules. The largest volume of groundfish is taken by trawl vessels; the number of such vessels is limited and each vessel in the limited entry trawl sector has been assigned a percentage of the overall quota for the sector or participates in a Pacific whiting cooperative. Fishermen in the limited entry fixed gear sector use line or pots and traps, primarily to catch sablefish. Vessels in the open access sector are generally smaller vessels using pots and lines and fish nearshore; this sector also includes trawlers who incidentally catch groundfish while fishing for pink shrimp, California halibut, ridgeback prawns, and sea cucumbers. Finally, commercial fishers who belong to one of five tribes with federally recognized treaty rights to fish for federally managed groundfish in their "usual and accustomed" fishing areas make up the tribal sector; these tribes, all of which are in Washington state, have formal allocations of sablefish and Pacific whiting, and receive allocations for other groundfish species annually through the PFMC. The individual states manage fishermen in the recreational sector in coordination with the PFMC.

Since 2000, West Coast groundfish fisheries management has been driven largely by the need to rebuild a number of species declared overfished: bocaccio, canary rockfish, cowcod, darkblotched rockfish, widow rockfish, Pacific ocean perch, petrale sole, and yelloweye rockfish. (Petrale sole and canary and widow rockfish have since been rebuilt). These species frequently co-occur with abundant groundfish that are targeted in the fishery; as a result, it is difficult for fishermen to avoid catching them. In order to accomplish stock rebuilding requirements, the PFMC established very low quotas for the overfished species and closed large areas, known as Rockfish Conservation Areas, to different types of fishing gear.

COASTAL PELAGIC SPECIES
FISHERY MANAGEMENT PLAN

Coastal pelagic species (CPS) are small, fast-growing species that form large schools in the water column. Off the west coast, they include northern anchovy, market squid, Pacific bonito, Pacific saury, Pacific herring, Pacific sardine, Pacific "chub" mackerel, jack mackerel, as well as other similar species. CPS populations can experience wide swings in abundance from year to year and over long periods in response to oceanographic conditions and competition among species for food. Since many other species of wildlife, including tunas, seabirds, and marine mammals, rely on them as food, these species and other similar species such as smelt are often referred to as "forage species." Under a separate Fishery Ecosystem Plan (described below), new fisheries for unmanaged and unfished forage species are prohibited, unless certain conditions are met.

The major CPS species generally are caught with "round-haul" gear such as purse seines, lampara nets, and dip nets, but also with trawls, gillnets, and other gear. CPS are caught by commercial fishermen and in smaller quantities by recreational fishermen on party or private boats.

Beyond the Exclusive Economic Zone, CPS are caught by Mexican and Canadian fishermen. Most of the catch of these species is exported to Asia and Europe.

Management of five of these species falls under the PFMC's CPS fishery management plan: Pacific sardine, Pacific mackerel, market squid, northern anchovy, and jack mackerel. The PFMC actively manages Pacific sardine, northern anchovy, and Pacific mackerel because of the size of the fisheries and markets, setting management measures for sardines in April, for mackerel in June, and for anchovy in November. Other species, such as market squid, are monitored by the PFMC but managed directly by the states. Since the current FMP went into effect in 1999, amendments have addressed bycatch, tribal fishing rights, fleet capacity and permit transferability, and seasonal allocation of catches. In 2006, the PFMC adopted an amendment to the CPS plan placing a ban on commercial fishing for all species of krill, making federal management consistent with management in California, Oregon, and Washington.

PACIFIC HALIBUT FISHERY MANAGEMENT

Pacific halibut, which range from northern California to the Bering Sea in Alaska, are much larger than California halibut, which is primarily caught south of Bodega Bay. While the PFMC has not developed an FMP for the Pacific halibut fishery, it does actively engage with the International Pacific Halibut Commission (IPHC) through NOAA Fisheries and through the IPHC's advisory bodies. Each year, the IPHC uses an updated stock assessment to estimate abundance and trends of Pacific halibut. It then sets a coastwide catch, which is allocated among the following sectors:

- Treaty Indian commercial as well as ceremonial and subsistence
- the following commercial non-Indian fisheries:
  - directed longline
  - incidental catch in the salmon troll fishery
  - incidental catch in the sablefish fishery north of Port Chehalis, Washington
- the sport fishery

The coastwide catch limit also is allocated among several regulatory areas. One of these areas is Area 2A, which covers waters off Washington, Oregon, and California. Under the Halibut Catch-Sharing Plan, the IPHC and NOAA Fisheries divide the total allowable catch for Area 2A among the three states, based partly on recommendations made by the PFMC each year in November.

In California, the Department and the Commission are responsible for setting annual regulations for sport fishing to implement the decisions of the IPHC and NOAA Fisheries. As recreational catches increased in recent years, the Department and California fishermen have become more involved in the IPHC process.

SALMON FISHERY MANAGEMENT PLAN

Unlike other species under PFMC management, salmon spend significant stages of their lives in freshwater streams and rivers and on the high seas beyond the U.S. Exclusive Economic Zone. As a result, these species are subject to an unusually wide range of environmental conditions beyond the control of the PFMC, ranging from the blocking of spawning areas by dams to periodic declines in prey in the ocean driven by climatic changes. In addition, a number of significant sub-populations of salmon have declined to the point that they are listed under the Endangered Species Act (ESA); avoiding capture of these sub-populations constrains fishing for more abundant populations with which they mingle in the ocean.

The two species that the PFMC focuses upon are Chinook and coho salmon. Chinook salmon spawn in freshwater streams and rivers as far as 2,000 miles from the ocean, while coho spawn in smaller rivers nearer the ocean. In all, ten "runs" of Chinook along the west coast are listed under the ESA, as are four runs of coho salmon. The PFMC's Salmon FMP includes two main elements: conservation objectives, which are expressed as number of spawners of the major stocks, and allocation provisions, which divide the allowed harvest among commercial, recreational, and tribal fishermen, and among various ports. The development of conservation objectives and allocation provisions begins in February of each year; the PFMC decides on the management of the fishery in April and NOAA Fisheries promulgates implementing regulations that are in effect from May 1 of the decision year to April 30 of the next year. Individual states adopt conforming regulations to manage the recreational fishery in their waters.

HIGHLY MIGRATORY SPECIES
FISHERY MANAGEMENT PLAN

The PFMC's fishery management plan for highly migratory species (HMS) includes the following species:

- tunas: Pacific albacore, yellowfin, bigeye, skipjack, and northern bluefin
- sharks: common thresher, pelagic thresher, bigeye thresher, shortfin mako, and blue
- billfish: Striped marlin and swordfish
- mahi-mahi

The catch of some other species, such as pelagic stingray and mola (ocean sunfish), is monitored, while the catch of other species, such as great white sharks, is prohibited and such fish must be released immediately. California commercial fishermen catch albacore with hook and line, swordfish with drift gillnets and harpoons, thresher sharks with drift gillnets, and bluefin and other tunas with purse seines. Recreational fishers fish for tunas, dorado, billfish, and sharks.

Because these species cross international boundaries, their management begins with regional fishery management organizations in the Pacific Ocean, primarily the Inter-American Tropical Tuna Commission (IATTC), whose jurisdiction is the Eastern Pacific Ocean, as well as the Western and Central Pacific Fisheries Commission (WCPFC). These regional fisheries management organizations may adopt non-binding resolutions or binding conservation and management measures that member countries must then implement. In recent years, both the IATTC and the WCPFC adopted measures to address overfishing of bigeye, yellowfin, and albacore tuna. In 2009, the WCPFC adopted such measures for bluefin tuna. Finally, the International Scientific Committee for Tuna and Tuna-Like Species in the North Pacific Ocean, whose members include the United States, China, Japan, and other North Pacific countries, conducts research and provides scientific advice to the IATTC and the WCPFC.

A further complication to managing highly migratory species is that, depending upon the species, U.S. management of HMS in the Pacific Ocean is under the jurisdiction of one or more councils: the PFMC, the Western Pacific Fishery Management Council, and the North Pacific Fishery Management Council.

The FMP for West Coast HMS, which NOAA Fisheries partially approved in 2004, was revised in 2011 in order to meet requirements of the Magnuson-Stevens Act amendments of 2006, requiring, among other elements, catch limits for some species and measures to avoid overfishing. Under the FMP, commercial fisheries must obtain a permit from NOAA Fisheries and maintain logbooks documenting their catch, as must recreational charter vessels. If requested by NOAA Fisheries, a vessel must carry a fishery observer. In recent years, the PFMC has used its biennial review of the FMP to make recommendations to NOAA Fisheries on catch limits for Bluefin tuna within overall limits set by the IATTC. It has also provided recommendations on any conservation measures for albacore tuna considered by the WCPFC, and has sent participants to workshops of the ISC.

FISHERY ECOSYSTEM PLAN

In April 2013, the PFMC adopted a Fishery Ecosystem Plan (FEP), Ecosystems Initiative Appendix, and a schedule for implementation. The geographical scope of the FEP is the U.S. portion of the California Current Ecosystem. The purpose of the FEP is "to enhance the Council's species-specific management programs with more ecosystem science, broader ecosystem considerations, and management policies that coordinate management across FMPs and the California Current Ecosystem." The FEP itself is informational, not regulatory. The PFMC intends to adjust the FEP over time by addressing emerging issues identified by assessing the status of initiatives under FEP and by revising priorities in odd-numbered years.

The FEP is intended to enhance management partly by assembling biophysical and socioeconomic information regarding climate change, habitat conditions, and ecosystem interactions. The FEP also will be used to identify and prioritize research needs, particularly regarding the cumulative effects of fisheries management on marine ecosystems and fishing communities. To this end, at each March meeting, the PFMC intends to review an annual report from NOAA Fisheries, the Annual State of the California Ecosystem, which aims to describe interactions within the California Current Ecosystem and to forecast how changing conditions and management actions may affect it.

The Ecosystems Initiative Appendix includes a list of issues that affect two or more Council FMPs and major policies that would benefit from coordination across FMPs in order to achieve ecosystem goals. In 2015, the list of FEP initiatives included the following, among others:

- protecting unfished and unmanaged forage fish species
- potential long-term effects of Council harvest policies on age- and size-distribution in managed stocks
- cross-FMP bycatch and catch monitoring policy
- new entrants to fisheries
- cross-FMP effects of climate-driven shifts in species distributions

In March 2015, the PFMC took action on the first of these initiatives when it decided to add currently unmanaged forage fish species, such as Pacific sand lances, smelt, and silversides, to all four FMPs and to prohibit the immediate development of new directed commercial fisheries on these species. In the future, new fisheries for these species will have to show both that they can be harvested sustainably and that a fishery would not harm ocean ecosystems.

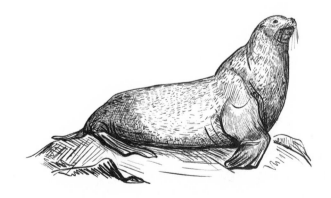

STATISTICAL PROFILES OF COMMERCIAL FISHERIES AT MAJOR CALIFORNIA PORTS IN 2014

(Total number of recorded species in parentheses)

SAN DIEGO AREA

PORT	2014 VOLUME (LBS)	2014 EX-VESSEL VALUE	TOP FIVE SPECIES (TOTAL SPECIES)
Mission Bay	998,920	$4,537,312	Spiny lobster, bigeye tuna, red sea urchin, spot prawn, opah (78)
Oceanside	701,049	$3,087,599	Spiny lobster, spot prawn, sablefish, shortspine thornyhead, ridgeback prawn (58)
San Diego	435,960	$2,322,512	Spiny lobster, swordfish, spot prawn, California sheephead, bigeye tuna (92)
Point Loma	205,448	$351,393	Red sea urchin, spiny lobster, California sheephead, swordfish, hagfishes (24)

LOS ANGELES AREA

PORT	2014 VOLUME (LBS)	2014 EX-VESSEL VALUE	TOP FIVE SPECIES (TOTAL SPECIES)
Terminal Island	32,253,590	$10,829,688	Market squid, spot prawn, red sea urchin, Pacific mackerel, yellowfin tuna (49)
San Pedro	22,537,177	$8,135,388	Market squid, spiny lobster, swordfish, Pacific mackerel, yellowfin tuna (70)
Dana Point	308,818	$2,040,832	Spiny lobster, shortspine thornyhead, spot prawn, red sea urchin, sablefish (44)
Newport Beach	218,323	$1,038,203	Spiny lobster, sablefish, shortspine thornyhead, spot prawn, sanddab (73)
Redondo Beach	298,993	$741,113	Spiny lobster, Pacific mackerel, yellow rock crab, hagfishes, red sea urchin (27)
Marina del Rey	104,637	$636,282	Spiny lobster, yellow rock crab, warty sea cucumber, spider crab, rock crab (26)
Long Beach	60,143	$553,833	Spiny lobster, ridgeback prawn, warty sea cucumber, California sheephead, spot prawn (19)
Avalon	50,166	$221,539	Spiny lobster, swordfish, yellowtail, sanddab, white seabass (26)

SANTA BARBARA AREA

PORT	2014 VOLUME (LBS)	2014 EX-VESSEL VALUE	TOP FIVE SPECIES (TOTAL SPECIES)
Ventura	37,872,362	$15,689,477	Market squid, spiny lobster, ridgeback prawn, spot prawn, bigeye tuna (106)
Santa Barbara	6,632,903	$12,981,970	Spiny lobster, red sea urchin, red rock crab, sablefish, yellow rock crab (112)
Port Hueneme	34,677,838	$11,507,240	Market squid, spot prawn, northern anchovy, Pacific mackerel, spiny lobster (18)
Oxnard	3,000,967	$4,284,517	Red sea urchin, spiny lobster, warty sea cucumber, spot prawn, white seabass (95)

MORRO BAY AREA

PORT	2014 VOLUME (LBS)	2014 EX-VESSEL VALUE	TOP FIVE SPECIES (TOTAL SPECIES)
Morro Bay	6,669,442	$8,297,265	Dungeness crab, sablefish, market squid, shortspine thornyhead, hagfishes (97)
Avila/ Port San Luis	458,043	$2,138,340	Dungeness crab, brown rockfish, gopher rockfish, cabezon, black-and-yellow rockfish (53)

MONTEREY AREA

PORT	2014 VOLUME (LBS)	2014 EX-VESSEL VALUE	TOP FIVE SPECIES (TOTAL SPECIES)
Monterey	67,655,229	$21,562,050	Market squid, Dungeness crab, spot prawn, Pacific sardine, northern anchovy (68)
Moss Landing	62,426,725	$16,324,605	Market squid, Dungeness crab, Northern anchovy, Pacific sardine, sablefish (81)
Santa Cruz	647,153	$2,363,247	Dungeness crab, Chinook salmon, California halibut, rock crab, white seabass (46)

SAN FRANCISCO AREA

PORT	2014 VOLUME (LBS)	2014 EX-VESSEL VALUE	TOP FIVE SPECIES (TOTAL SPECIES)
San Francisco	19,259,945	$26,240,268	Dungeness crab, Chinook salmon. market squid, swordfish, Pacific herring roe (98)
Princeton-Half Moon Bay	20,617,258	$16,812,735	Dungeness crab, market squid, Chinook salmon, spot prawn, California halibut (77)
Vallejo	696,281	$2,146,610	Dungeness crab, bay shrimp, California halibut, staghorn sculpin, coonstriped shrimp (7)
Berkeley	52,210	$266,798	California halibut, Chinook salmon, Dungeness carb, rock crab, lingcod (35)
Alameda	35,955	$165,705	Dungeness crab, rock crab, Chinook salmon, California halibut, blue rockfish (7)
Sausalito	13,570	$50,677	Dungeness crab, Chinook salmon, California halibut, brown rockfish, lingcod (11)

BODEGA BAY AREA

PORT	2014 VOLUME (LBS)	2014 EX-VESSEL VALUE	TOP FIVE SPECIES (TOTAL SPECIES)
Bodega Bay	4,161,218	$12,861,114	Dungeness crab, Chinook salmon, sablefish, hagfishes, market squid (38)
Bolinas	107,290	$445,518	Dungeness crab, Chinook salmon, sablefish, California halibut, night smelt (11)

FORT BRAGG AREA

PORT	2014 VOLUME (LBS)	2014 EX-VESSEL VALUE	TOP FIVE SPECIES (TOTAL SPECIES)
Fort Bragg	7,462,923	$12,960,666	Chinook salmon, Dungeness crab, red sea urchin, sablefish, Petrale sole (76)
Point Arena	793,221	$971,459	Red sea urchin, Chinook salmon, Dungeness crab, cabezon, gopher rockfish (17)
Albion	597,247	$418,464	Red sea urchin, Chinook salmon, cabezon, kelp greenling, black-and-yellow rockfish (15)

EUREKA AREA

PORT	2014 VOLUME (LBS)	2014 EX-VESSEL VALUE	TOP FIVE SPECIES (TOTAL SPECIES)
Eureka	14,511,406	$14,474,545	Dungeness crab, market squid, sablefish, albacore tuna, ocean pink shrimp (48)
Crescent City	9,360,800	$13,204,257	Dungeness crab, ocean pink shrimp, coonstriped shrimp, sablefish, black rockfish (33)
Trinidad	738,600	$3,110,559	Dungeness crab, lingcod, Chinook salmon (3)
Fields Landing	584,914	$400,043	Hagfishes, Dungeness crab (2)
Shelter Cove	84,580	$357,613	Dungeness crab, Chinook salmon, lingcod, black rockfish, blue rockfish (17)

COMMON FISHING GEAR
AND METHODS

As fishermen of different nationalities settled in California in the last 150 years, they introduced different methods of fishing from their home countries. The Portuguese fishermen who settled in the San Diego area introduced pole-and-line fishing for tuna. Italian and Yugoslavian fishermen who settled in San Pedro perfected the use of purse seines and introduced the power block for catching squid and sardines. Italian fishermen from the Ligurian Sea took up fishing in the Santa Barbara area, using traps to catch lobster and gillnets or hook-and-line to catch fish. In more recent years, fishermen from Vietnam have used gillnets in catching rockfish and nearshore species such as halibut and croaker.

Technological innovations spurred by the war effort during World War II brought still more changes to fishing technology. Besides the use of steel and lightweight fiberglass for boat hulls, war research developed lightweight synthetic nylon yarns that enabled the manufacture of larger, lighter nets. More powerful and reliable engines enabled fishermen to get to and from fishing grounds more quickly, while onboard refrigeration ensured that their catch did not spoil. Electronic equipment such as sonar, radar, and GPS made it possible for fishermen to locate and relocate particular areas of the ocean with unprecedented accuracy and to locate schools of fish.

Innovation has continued. Satellite communications have made it possible for fishermen to communicate regularly and reliably with shore and among themselves, and to return to productive fishing grounds or to retrieve nets and traps. Satellite sensors also have provided fishermen with real-time pictures of currents and areas of productive waters, allowing them to search more efficiently for billfish or schools of tuna, for instance.

Off California, commercial fishermen use several basic types of fishing gear, including nets, hooks and lines, and traps, among others.

GILLNETS

Gillnets are panels of net that may have different dimensions. Gillnets may be fished on the bottom, in midwater, or at the surface, and the size of their mesh—that is the openings in the net—will vary depending on the species of fish being sought. Regulations often set a minimum mesh size that is small enough to catch the "target" species of a particular size, but large enough to allow juvenile or other small fish to escape. For instance, the minimum mesh size for a drift gill net for swordfish or thresher shark is 14 inches measured diagonally between knots, whereas the minimum mesh size for white seabass is 6 inches.

If the panel of net is set taut, fish become ensnared as they attempt to back out of the net and become caught either in their midsection or by their gills. When the net is set more loosely, it is called a trammel net. With this gear, fish become entangled as a fin or other part of the body becomes snagged and the fish becomes increasingly enmeshed as it struggles to free itself.

Gillnets may be fixed to the bottom or may be attached to a vessel that drifts with the currents. Depending on the species being sought, drift gillnets are set at or below the surface. When fishing for seabass or barracuda, for instance, fishermen set their nets at the surface and drift during the day. When fishing for swordfish or sharks, fishermen set their nets below the surface and drift at night. The size of the mesh differs, also. To catch barracuda, fishermen use nets with a mesh size of three inches.

Over the years, the legislature adopted restrictions on the use of gillnets in many nearshore areas because of declines in some nearshore fish populations, conflicts with other fisheries, and the incidental capture and drowning of seabirds and marine mammals. Proposition 132, passed by the voters in 1990, created a Marine Resources Protection Zone within three miles of the mainland coast, and in waters less than 70 fathoms or within one nautical mile of the Channel Islands, whichever is less. The initiative banned the use of gill and trammel nets in these waters beginning in 1994.

TRAWLS

Trawls are sock-shaped nets that taper from a wide mouth to a narrow tail called a codend. Trawls are towed behind a fishing vessel along the bottom or in midwater, depending on the species sought. The mesh sizes in trawls vary as well. For instance, ridgeback prawn trawls use 1½ inch mesh, midwater trawls use 3-inch mesh to catch whiting and widow rockfish, groundfish trawls use 5 inch mesh, and trawls targeting California halibut use 7½ inch mesh. Any organism that is larger than the size mesh in the trawl is captured and accumulates in the codend.

The rope or cable on the lower leading edge of a trawl towed along the bottom is usually protected by chain sinkers that stir organisms up from the sea bottom. The bottom rope may also be protected by rubber disks or bobbins that allow a trawl to be dragged over hard bottom that might otherwise snag the net. Such trawls are called roller rigs. Bottom trawls also vary in how high their opening is. Trawls used to catch shrimp and groundfish, for instance, have a low opening, whereas trawls fishing for other species have a high opening. The mouth of trawls may be held wide by otter boards that are attached to the two forward corners of the net; the boards act like wings and pull the net wide as it moves through the water.

ROUND-HAUL NET

There are two types of round-haul nets: the lampara net and the purse-seine net. These nets are used to catch sardines, anchovies, herring, market squid, bonito, mackerel, and tuna. Both types of round-haul nets consist of long panels of netting that are used to encircle a school of fish. The nets are pulled from the deck of a vessel by a skiff so that the net surrounds the fish. After a lampara net is deployed, the leadline at the bottom of the net is pulled until it closes the net into a scoop, and the catch is brought on board the boat.

A purse-seine net ends in a smaller-meshed landing bag. When the net has been set by the skiff, a line running through rings at the bottom of the net is drawn closed like a purse string. The rings then are brought aboard, and the wings of the net are pulled aboard with a power block. The catch is captured in the bag of the net. Many fishermen now use drum seines, which retrieve the net via a large reel mounted at the stern of the vessel. Purse seines are used to catch tuna, mackerel, squid, sardines, and anchovies.

HOOK AND LINE

California fishermen use several types of hook and line fishing methods. The most familiar perhaps is the rod and reel, in which one or more hooks is attached to a line that runs along a pole and is retracted by means of a mechanical reel. Whether or not a pole is used, reels may be hand-powered or mechanized, and used in both commercial and recreational fisheries.

In California, where surface or so-called pelagic longlines are prohibited, set longlines may be used. These are lines of hooks run horizontally across the seafloor. The line is held in place by anchors, while floats suspend the line above the seafloor, with hooks attached at regular intervals. In some areas along the California coast, no more than 150 hooks may be attached to set longlines. This gear is used to catch rockfish and sablefish.

A related type of hook-and-line gear is called stick gear, which is used almost entirely in the nearshore fishery for live fish. Stick gear is a series of hooks attached to a weighted rod by short lines. This gear is placed on the seafloor.

In jigging, a vertical line of lures is moved up and down by hand or mechanically. This method is used principally to catch squid.

In using troll gear to catch salmon, up to six stainless steel lines are run from hydraulic spools to outrigger poles from which they are spread and suspended from the boat. Hooks, baited with herring or anchovy or with artificial lures, are attached to the mainline with monofilament leaders at roughly 18-foot intervals. A weight attached to the end of each wire line keeps the line at a particular depth. The lines are then pulled slowly through the water—an activity called "trolling." To catch albacore tuna, fishermen use a simpler arrangement of several lines towed on the surface.

TRAP OR POT

Traps are generally constructed of galvanized wire that may or may not be vinyl coated. Escape ports or rings allow undersized lobsters, crabs, or fish to escape. Metal fastenings or cotton twine dissolve after a time in sea water allowing the catch to escape if the trap is lost. Buoys painted with the fisherman's permit number are attached to strings of traps. As winter arrives, traps are set in deeper and deeper water. Commercial fishermen use traps to catch spot prawns, spiny lobster, Dungeness crabs, rock crabs, rockfish, sablefish, hagfish, cabezon, and sheephead. Recreational fishermen use different types of traps to catch Dungeness and rock crabs and spiny lobster.

DIVING GEAR

In taking sea urchins or sea cucumbers, commercial divers use a "hookah" system, rather than the usual tank we associate with scuba diving. A hookah system is simply a long air hose attached to an air compressor on the deck of a boat. Divers may spend as long as six hours a day underwater. Animals are harvested by hand, so that the rate of harvest depends on the diver, not the size of the boat. Some recreational spear fishermen use SCUBA to spear nearshore fishes, while others free dive without SCUBA when fishing for abalone north of San Francisco, or for finfish elsewhere in the state.

Different types of gear dominate the catches of different species, although there often is a mix. In 2014, according to statistics maintained by NOAA Fisheries, half of all catches of California halibut were in trawls and another 39 percent on hand lines. In the same year, 84 percent of commercially landed California sheephead were caught in traps, while the balance was caught largely with hand lines. Similarly, any one type of gear may be used to catch a variety of species. For example, so-called light touch trawls may be used to catch California halibut, angel shark, sea cucumber, skates, sole, and white seabass, while one type of trap may be used to catch red crab, brown crab, yellow crab, Dungeness crab, Kellet's whelk, or octopus.

The size of vessels used by California fishermen ranges widely, from skiffs and kayaks in the nearshore live-fish fishery to large purse seiners in the squid, tuna, and mackerel fisheries. Most fishing vessels, from trawlers to trap boats, fall between these two extremes. Size plays a major role in who fishes in some areas. Generally, large vessels are more mobile, able to move from area to area, to fish at night, and to stay offshore, while smaller vessels are more resident and more likely to be day-boats.

Finally, catching and landing fish and shellfish is but one step in a process that includes processing, distributing, preparing, and consuming seafood products. According to NOAA Fisheries statistics for 2014, there were 45 processors employing 1,047 people in California, as well as 365 wholesalers employing 4,582 people.

ABOUT THE AUTHORS

MICHAEL L. WEBER provides strategic advice for oceans, coasts, and fisheries programs at Resources Legacy Fund. His most recent past position was as advisor to the California Fish and Game Commission in the implementation of the Marine Life Management Act. Previously, Mike directed programs on marine protected areas, sea turtle conservation, and fisheries conservation at the Center for Marine Conservation in Washington, DC. He also worked as special assistant to the director of the National Marine Fisheries Service in the U.S. Department of Commerce. Mike has written books, articles, and reports on a wide range of ocean issues, and has advised in the production of television specials and exhibits on marine conservation. He and Burr Heneman wrote the first edition of the *Guide to the Marine Life Management Act* in 2000. Mike lives with his wife in Sacramento.

BURR HENEMAN negotiated and drafted the Marine Life Management Act at the request of then-Assemblyman Fred Keeley, author of the legislation (1997–'98). Subsequently, he initiated a public/private partnership that provided outside advisors and funding to help the Fish and Game Commission and the Department of Fish and Wildlife implement the MLMA (1999–2005). He became interested in fishery management reform while serving on a Pacific Fishery Management Council advisory panel (1992–'96). He got a similar grounding in California's fishery management while writing legislation that phased out nearshore gill net fisheries in Central and Northern California (1980–'86). His career has included oil spill prevention and response, including in Alaska for the *Exxon Valdez* oil spill (1989) and in Saudi Arabia for the Gulf War oil spill and fires (1991). He was a consultant on marine debris to the Marine Mammal Commission when that issue was first emerging as an international concern (1984–'88). More recently (2005–'09), he developed the Packard Foundation's global seabird conservation program.

HUFF MCGONIGAL is the Principal at Fathom Consulting, providing strategic guidance and support to clients in the fields of marine policy, science, and law. Prior to founding Fathom Consulting in 2006, Huff worked with Environmental Defense Fund as a Senior Project Manager, working to advance fisheries policy change and improvement projects. Prior to that he worked as a Marine Policy Coordinator for the Monterey Bay National Marine Sanctuary helping the Sanctuary engage stakeholders to address issues ranging from habitat protection to water quality, desalination, and coastal development. Previously, Huff worked with the California Department of Fish and Wildlife examining the effectiveness of marine reserves and as a commercial diver. Huff earned his Juris Doctorate from Lewis and Clark Law School in Portland, Oregon. He lives in Santa Barbara with his wife and three children.

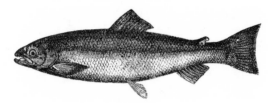